Celebrate Recovery®
Inside

PARTICIPANT'S GUIDES

A recovery program based on
eight principles from the Beatitudes

JOHN BAKER

FOREWORD BY RICK WARREN

ZONDERVAN™

GRAND RAPIDS, MICHIGAN 49530 USA

ZONDERVAN™

Celebrate Recovery® Inside
Copyright © 1998 by John Baker

Requests for information should be addressed to:

Zondervan, *Grand Rapids, Michigan 49530*

ISBN-10: 0-310-60279-3
ISBN-13: 978-0-310-60279-8

Interior design by Michelle Espinoza

Printed in the United States of America

13 14 15 16 /❖ DCI/ 20 19 18 17 16 15 14 13 12 11

Celebrate Recovery®

Stepping Out of
Denial into God's Grace

PARTICIPANT'S GUIDE 1

John Baker is the founder of Celebrate Recovery®, a ministry born out of the heart of Saddleback Church. Over the last fourteen years, more than 7,500 individuals have gone through this Christ-centered recovery program at Saddleback. The Celebrate Recovery program is now being used in thousands of churches nationwide. In 1993, John and Pastor Rick Warren wrote the Celebrate Recovery curriculum which has been published and translated into several languages.

John began serving at Saddleback as a lay pastor in 1991. In 1992, he was asked to join the Saddleback Church staff as the Director of Small Groups and Recovery. In 1995, his responsibilities increased as he became the Pastor of Membership. In this position, John's responsibilities included pastoral counseling, pastoral care, Celebrate Recovery, support groups, small groups, and family, singles, and recreation ministries. In 1996, he oversaw the development of Saddleback's lay counseling ministry.

In June 1997, John became the Pastor of Ministries, responsible for the recruitment, training, and deployment of church members to serve in one of the more than 156 different ministries at Saddleback.

In 2001, Rick Warren asked John to become the Pastor of Celebrate Recovery. This is John's shape, his passion, and his calling. In addition, he is part of Saddleback's Purpose Driven team. John is a nationally known speaker and trainer in helping churches start Celebrate Recovery ministries. These ministries, in thousands of churches, reach out not only to their congregations but also to their communities in helping those dealing with a hurt, hang-up, or habit.

John and his wife Cheryl have been married thirty-five years and have served together in Celebrate Recovery since 1991. They have two adult children, Laura and Johnny. In 2004, Johnny and his wife, Jeni, gave John and Cheryl their first grandchild, Maggie.

UPDATED EDITION

Celebrate Recovery®

Stepping Out of Denial into God's Grace

PARTICIPANT'S GUIDE 1

A recovery program based on
eight principles from the Beatitudes

JOHN BAKER

FOREWORD BY RICK WARREN

GRAND RAPIDS, MICHIGAN 49530 USA

CONTENTS

FOREWORD BY RICK WARREN

You've undoubtedly heard the expression "Time heals all wounds." Unfortunately, it isn't true. As a pastor I frequently talk with people who are still carrying hurts from thirty or forty years ago. The truth is, time often makes things worse. Wounds that are left untended fester and spread infection throughout your entire body. Time only extends the pain if the problem isn't dealt with.

Celebrate Recovery® is a biblical and balanced program that can help you overcome your hurts, habits, and hang-ups. Based on the actual words of Jesus rather than psychological theory, this recovery program is more effective in helping people change than anything else I've seen or heard of. Over the years I've witnessed how the Holy Spirit has used this program to transform literally thousands of lives at Saddleback Church and help people grow toward full Christlike maturity.

Perhaps you are familiar with the classic 12-Step program of AA and other groups. While undoubtedly many lives have been helped through the 12 Steps, I've always been uncomfortable with that program's vagueness about the nature of God, the saving power of Jesus Christ, and the ministry of the Holy Spirit. So I began an intense study of the Scriptures to discover what God had to say about "recovery." To my amazement, I found the principles of recovery—in their logical order—given by Christ in His most famous message, the Sermon on the Mount.

My study resulted in a ten-week series of messages called "The Road to Recovery." During that series my associate pastor John Baker developed the four participant's guides, which became the heart of our Celebrate Recovery program.

As you work through these participant's guides, I trust that you will come to realize many benefits from this program. Most of all, however, my prayer for you is that, through Celebrate Recovery, you will find deep peace and lasting freedom in Jesus Christ as you walk your own road to recovery.

Dr. Rick Warren
Senior Pastor, Saddleback Church

INTRODUCTION

Welcome to the "Road to Recovery." You are in for an exciting and amazing journey as you take the hand of the true and only Higher Power, Jesus Christ, and walk with Him toward healing and serenity.

The purpose of this program is to allow us to become free from life's hurts, hang-ups, and habits. By working through the eight recovery principles found in the Beatitudes with Jesus Christ as your Higher Power, you can and will change! You will begin to experience the true peace and serenity you have been seeking, and you will no longer have to rely on your dysfunctional, compulsive, and addictive behaviors as a temporary "fix" for your pain.

By applying the biblical principles of conviction, conversion, surrender, confession, restitution, prayer, quiet time, witnessing, and helping one another, which are found within the eight principles and the Christ-centered 12 Steps, you will restore and develop stronger relationships with others and with God.

To begin our journey, we will need to step out of denial and into God's grace. This is what working through Principles 1–3 will help us accomplish. We begin by looking at the toll *denial* has had on our ability to face the reality of our past and present. Then we need to admit that we are *powerless* over certain areas of our lives, and that, alone, we do not have the power to control them.

In Principle 2, we find the *hope* that our Higher Power, Jesus Christ, can restore us to *sanity* and that through Him alone we can find the power to help us recover. And finally, in Principle 3, we take the *action* to *turn* our lives and our wills over to His care and direction.

After each lesson, there is an exercise for you to complete. Answer each question to the best of your ability. Don't worry about what you think the answer *should* be. Pray and then write down the answer from your heart. Remember John 8:32: "Then you will know the truth, and the truth will set you free."

After you have completed the exercise, share it with someone you trust. Your group, an accountability partner, your sponsor (someone farther along in recovery who has agreed to be your "travel guide"; sponsors are explained in Participant's Guide 2, Lesson 8), or a close friend in recovery are all choices. You do not recover from your hurts, hang-ups, and habits just by attending recovery meetings. You must work and live following the eight principles of recovery found in the Beatitudes and the 12 Steps and their biblical comparisons. God bless you as you walk this road.

In His steps,
John Baker

THE ROAD TO RECOVERY

Eight Principles Based on the Beatitudes

By Pastor Rick Warren

1. **R**ealize I'm not God. I admit that I am powerless to control my tendency to do the wrong thing and that my life is unmanageable.
   "Happy are those who know they are spiritually poor."
   (Matthew 5:3)

2. **E**arnestly believe that God exists, that I matter to Him, and that He has the power to help me recover.
   "Happy are those who mourn, for they shall be comforted."
   (Matthew 5:4)

3. **C**onsciously choose to commit all my life and will to Christ's care and control.
   "Happy are the meek." (Matthew 5:5)

4. **O**penly examine and confess my faults to myself, to God, and to someone I trust.
   "Happy are the pure in heart." (Matthew 5:8)

5. **V**oluntarily submit to every change God wants to make in my life and humbly ask Him to remove my character defects.
   "Happy are those whose greatest desire is to do what God requires."
   (Matthew 5:6)

6. **E**valuate all my relationships. Offer forgiveness to those who have hurt me and make amends for harm I've done to others, except when to do so would harm them or others.
   "Happy are the merciful." (Matthew 5:7)
   "Happy are the peacemakers." (Matthew 5:9)

7. **R**eserve a daily time with God for self-examination, Bible reading, and prayer in order to know God and His will for my life and to gain the power to follow His will.

8. **Y**ield myself to God to be used to bring this Good News to others, both by my example and by my words.
   "Happy are those who are persecuted because they
   do what God requires." (Matthew 5:10)

Twelve Steps and
Their Biblical Comparisons

1. We admitted we were powerless over our addictions and compulsive
    behaviors, that our lives had become unmanageable.

    "I know that nothing good lives in me, that is, in my sinful nature.
    For I have the desire to do what is good, but I cannot carry it out."
    (Romans 7:18)

2. We came to believe that a power greater than ourselves could restore
    us to sanity.

    "For it is God who works in you to will and to act according
    to his good purpose." (Philippians 2:13)

3. We made a decision to turn our lives and our wills over to the care of God.

    "Therefore, I urge you, brothers, in view of God's mercy, to offer
    your bodies as living sacrifices, holy and pleasing to God—
    this is your spiritual act of worship." (Romans 12:1)

4. We made a searching and fearless moral inventory of ourselves.

    "Let us examine our ways and test them, and let us return
    to the Lord." (Lamentations 3:40)

5. We admitted to God, to ourselves, and to another human being the
    exact nature of our wrongs.

    "Therefore confess your sins to each other and pray for each other
    so that you may be healed." (James 5:16)

6. We were entirely ready to have God remove all these defects of character.

    "Humble yourselves before the Lord, and he will lift you up."
    (James 4:10)

7. We humbly asked Him to remove all our shortcomings.

   "If we confess our sins, he is faithful and just and will forgive us our sins and purify us from all unrighteousness." (1 John 1:9)

8. We made a list of all persons we had harmed and became willing to make amends to them all.

   "Do to others as you would have them do to you." (Luke 6:31)

9. We made direct amends to such people whenever possible, except when to do so would injure them or others.

   "Therefore, if you are offering your gift at the altar and there remember that your brother has something against you, leave your gift there in front of the altar. First go and be reconciled to your brother; then come and offer your gift." (Matthew 5:23–24)

10. We continued to take personal inventory and when we were wrong, promptly admitted it.

    "So, if you think you are standing firm, be careful that you don't fall!" (1 Corinthians 10:12)

11. We sought through prayer and meditation to improve our conscious contact with God, praying only for knowledge of His will for us and power to carry that out.

    "Let the word of Christ dwell in you richly." (Colossians 3:16)

12. Having had a spiritual experience as the result of these steps, we try to carry this message to others and to practice these principles in all our affairs.

    "Brothers, if someone is caught in a sin, you who are spiritual should restore him gently. But watch yourself, or you also may be tempted." (Galatians 6:1)

SERENITY PRAYER

If you have attended secular recovery programs, you have seen the first four lines of the "Prayer for Serenity." The following is the complete prayer. I encourage you to pray it daily as you work through the principles!

Prayer for Serenity

God, grant me the serenity
to accept the things I cannot change,
the courage to change the things I can,
and the wisdom to know the difference.
Living one day at a time,
enjoying one moment at a time;
accepting hardship as a pathway to peace;
taking, as Jesus did,
this sinful world as it is,
not as I would have it;
trusting that You will make all things right
if I surrender to Your will;
so that I may be reasonably happy in this life
and supremely happy with You forever in the next.
Amen.

Reinhold Niebuhr

CELEBRATE RECOVERY'S SMALL GROUP GUIDELINES

The following five guidelines will ensure that your small group is a safe place. They need to be read at the beginning of every meeting.

1. Keep your sharing focused on your own thoughts and feelings. Limit your sharing to three to five minutes.
2. There is NO cross talk. Cross talk is when two individuals engage in conversation excluding all others. Each person is free to express his or her feelings without interruptions.
3. We are here to support one another, not "fix" another.
4. Anonymity and confidentiality are basic requirements. What is shared in the group stays in the group. The only exception is when someone threatens to injure themselves or others.
5. Offensive language has no place in a Christ-centered recovery group.

DENIAL

Principle 1: Realize I'm not God. I admit that I am powerless to control my tendency to do the wrong thing and that my life is unmanageable.

"Happy are those who know they are spiritually poor."
(Matthew 5:3)

Step 1: We admitted we were powerless over our addictions and compulsive behaviors, that our lives had become unmanageable.

"I know that nothing good lives in me, that is, in my sinful nature. For I have the desire to do what is good, but I cannot carry it out."
(Romans 7:18)

Think About It

Before we can take the first step of our recovery, we must first face and admit our denial.

God tells us, "You can't heal a wound by saying it's not there!" (Jeremiah 6:14, TLB). The acrostic for DENIAL spells out what can happen if we do not face our denial.

Disables our feelings

By repressing our feelings we freeze our emotions. Understanding and feeling our feelings is freedom.

"They promise them freedom, while they themselves are slaves
of destructive habits—for a man is a slave of anything that
has conquered him." (2 Peter 2:19, GNB)

Energy lost

A side effect of our denial is anxiety. Anxiety causes us to waste precious energy running from our past and worrying about and dreading the future. It is only in the present, today, where positive change can occur.

"He frees the prisoners . . .; he lifts the burdens from those bent down
beneath their loads." (Psalm 146:7–8, TLB)

Negates growth

We are "as sick as our secrets." We cannot grow in recovery until we are ready to step out of our denial into the truth.

"They cried to the Lord in their troubles, and he rescued them! He
led them from their darkness and shadow of death and snapped
their chains." (Psalm 107:13–14, TLB)

Isolates us from God

God's light shines on the truth. Our denial keeps us in the dark.

"God is light; in him there is no darkness at all. If we claim to have
fellowship with him yet walk in the darkness, we lie and do not live
by the truth. But if we walk in the light, as he is in the light,
we have fellowship with one another, and the blood of Jesus,
his Son, purifies us from all sin." (1 John 1:5–7)

Alienates us from our relationships

Denial tells us we are getting away with it. We think no one knows—but they do.

What is the answer?

"Stop lying to each other; tell the truth, for we are parts of each other and when we lie to each other we are hurting ourselves."
(Ephesians 4:25, TLB)

Lengthens the pain

We have the false belief that denial protects us from our pain. In reality, denial allows our pain to fester and grow and turn into *shame* and *guilt*.

> *God's promise: "I will give you back your health again and heal your wounds." (Jeremiah 30:17, TLB)*

Accept the first principle of recovery. Step out of your denial! Step into your Higher Power's—Jesus Christ's—unconditional love and grace!

Write About It

1. What areas of your life do you have power (control) over? Be specific.

2. What areas of your life are out of control, unmanageable? Be specific.

3. How do you think taking this first step will help you?

4. As a child, what coping skills did you use to get attention or to protect yourself?

5. In your family of origin, what was the "family secret" that everyone was trying to protect?

6. How do you handle pain and disappointment?

7. How can you begin to address your denial?

8. In what areas of your life are you now beginning to face reality and break the effects of denial?

9. Are you starting to develop a support team? Are you asking for phone numbers in your meetings?

   List them here or on the inside back cover of this participant's guide!

POWERLESS

Principle 1: Realize I'm not God. I admit that I am powerless to control my tendency to do the wrong thing and that my life is unmanageable."

"Happy are those who know they are spiritually poor."
(Matthew 5:3)

Step 1: We admitted we were powerless over our addictions and compulsive behaviors, that our lives had become unmanageable.

"I know that nothing good lives in me, that is, in my sinful nature.
For I have the desire to do what is good, but I cannot carry it out."
(Romans 7:18)

Think About It

When we accept the first recovery principle and take that first step out of our denial and into reality, we see there are very few things that we really have control over. Once we admit that by ourselves we are powerless we can stop living with the following "serenity robbers," spelled out in the acrostic POWERLESS.

Pride

Ignorance + power + pride = a deadly mixture!

"Pride ends in a fall, while humility brings honor."
(Proverbs 29:23, TLB)

Only ifs

Our "only ifs" in life keep us trapped in the fantasyland of rationalization!

"Whatever is covered up will be uncovered, and every secret will be made known. So then, whatever you have said in the dark will be heard in broad daylight." (Luke 12:2–3, GNB)

Worry

Worrying is a form of not trusting God enough!

"So don't be anxious about tomorrow. God will take care of your tomorrow too. Live one day at a time." (Matthew 6:34, TLB)

Escape

By living in denial we may have escaped into a world of fantasy and unrealistic expectations of ourselves and others.

"For light is capable of showing up everything for what it really is. It is even possible for light to turn the thing it shines upon into light also." (Ephesians 5:13–14, PH)

Resentments

Resentments act like an emotional cancer if they are allowed to fester and grow.

"'In your anger do not sin': Do not let the sun go down while you are still angry, and do not give the devil a foothold." (Ephesians 4:26–27)

Loneliness

Loneliness is a choice. In recovery and in Christ, you never have to walk alone.

"Continue to love each other with true brotherly love. Don't forget to be kind to strangers, for some who have done this have entertained angels without realizing it!" (Hebrews 13:1–2, TLB)

Emptiness

You know that empty feeling deep inside. The cold wind of hopelessness blows right through it.

> *Jesus said, "My purpose is to give life in all its fullness."*
> *(John 10:10, TLB)*

Selfishness

We often pray: "Our Father which art in heaven; give me, give me, give me."

> *"Whoever clings to his life shall lose it, and whoever loses his life*
> *shall save it." (Luke 17:33, TLB)*

Separation

Some people talk about finding God—as if He could ever get lost!

> *"For I am convinced that nothing can ever separate us from his love.*
> *Death can't, and life can't. The angels won't, and all the powers of*
> *hell itself cannot keep God's love away. . . . Nothing will ever be able*
> *to separate us from the love God demonstrated by our Lord Jesus*
> *Christ when he died for us." (Romans 8:38–39, TLB)*

Congratulations! In your admission of your powerlessness you have begun the journey of recovery that will allow you to accept the true and only Higher Power's—Jesus Christ's—healing, love, and forgiveness.

At this stage in your recovery, you need to *stop* doing two things:

1. Stop Denying the Pain

You are ready to take your first step in recovery when your pain is greater than your fear.

> *"Pity me, O Lord, for I am weak. Heal me, for my body is sick, and*
> *I am upset and disturbed. My mind is filled with apprehension and*
> *with gloom." (Psalm 6:2–3, TLB)*

2. Stop Playing God

You are unable to do for yourself what you need God to do for you. You are either going to serve God or yourself. You can't serve both.

> *"No one can be a slave to two masters; he will hate one and love the other; he will be loyal to one and despise the other."*
> *(Matthew 6:24, GNB)*

In addition to stopping certain behaviors, you need to start doing two things:

1. Start Admitting Your Powerlessness

As you work the first principle, you will see that by yourself you do not have the power to change your hurts, hang-ups, and habits.

> *"Jesus . . . said, 'With man this is impossible, but with God all things are possible.'" (Matthew 19:26)*

2. Start Admitting That Your Life Has Become Unmanageable

You can finally start admitting that some or all areas of your life are out of your control to change.

> *"Problems far too big for me to solve are piled higher than my head. Meanwhile my sins, too many to count, have all caught up with me and I am ashamed to look up." (Psalm 40:12, TLB).*

Principle 1 Prayer

> *Dear God, Your Word tells me that I can't heal my hurts, hang-ups, and habits by just saying that they are not there. Help me! Parts of my life, or all of my life, are out of control. I now know that I cannot "fix" myself. It seems the harder that I try to do the right thing the more I struggle. Lord, I want to step out of my denial into the truth. I pray for You to show me the way. In Your Son's name I pray, Amen.*

Note: Before you begin "Write About It," read the "Prayer for Serenity" on page 14 and read the Principle 1 verses on page 31.

Write About It

1. List some of the ways that your pride has stopped you from asking for and getting the help you need to overcome your hurts, hang-ups, and habits.

2. What in your past has caused you to have the "if onlys"?

   "If only" I had stopped _____ years ago.

   "If only" _____ hadn't left me.

3. Instead of worrying about things that we cannot control, we need to focus on what God can do in our lives. What are you worrying about? Why?

4. In what ways have you tried to escape your past pain? Be specific.

5. How has holding on to your anger and your resentments affected you?

6. Do you believe that loneliness is a choice? Why or why not? How has your denial isolated you from your important relationships?

7. Describe the emptiness you feel and some new ways you are finding to fill it?

8. Selfishness is at the heart of most problems between people. In what areas of your life have you been selfish?

9. Separation from God can feel very real, but it is never permanent. What can you do to get closer to God?

Principle 1 Verses

"You can't heal a wound by saying it's not there!"
(Jeremiah 6:14, TLB)

*"If you wait for perfect conditions, you will never
get anything done." (Ecclesiastes 11:4, TLB)*

*"My heart is troubled and restless. Waves of affliction
have come upon me." (Job 30:27 TLB)*

*"I don't understand myself at all, for I really want to do what is
right, but I can't. I do what I don't want to—what I hate. I know
perfectly well that what I am doing is wrong, and my bad conscience proves that I agree with these laws I am breaking. But I can't
help myself, because I'm no longer doing it. It is sin inside me that is
stronger than I am that makes me do these evil things."
(Romans 7:15–17, TLB)*

*"Before every man there lies a wide and pleasant road that seems
right but ends in death." (Proverbs 14:12, TLB)*

*"My good days are in the past. My hopes have disappeared.
My heart's desires are broken." (Job 17:11, TLB)*

*"I am worn out with pain; every night my pillow is wet with tears.
My eyes are growing old and dim with grief because of
all my enemies." (Psalm 6:6–7, TLB)*

*"We felt we were doomed to die and saw how powerless we were
to help ourselves." (2 Corinthians 1:9, TLB)*

HOPE

Principle 2: Earnestly believe that God exists, that I matter to Him, and that He has the power to help me recover.

"Happy are those who mourn, for they shall be comforted."
(Matthew 5:4)

Step 2: We came to believe that a power greater than ourselves could restore us to sanity.

"For it is God who works in you to will and to act according to his good purpose." (Philippians 2:13)

Think About It

"Anyone who comes to God must believe that he exists and that he rewards those who earnestly seek him." (Hebrews 11:6)

In the first principle, we admitted we were powerless. Now in the second principle, we come to believe God exists, that we are important to Him, and that we are able to receive God's power to help us recover. It's in the second step we find HOPE!

Higher Power

Our Higher Power has a name: Jesus Christ! Jesus desires a hands-on, day-to-day, moment-to-moment relationship with us. He can do for us what we have never been able to do for ourselves.

"Everything comes from God alone. Everything lives by his power."
(Romans 11:36, TLB)

Our Higher Power tells us, "My grace is enough for you: for where
there is weakness, my power is shown the more completely."
(2 Corinthians 12:9, PH)

Openness to change

Throughout our lives, we will continue to encounter hurts and trials that we are powerless to change. With God's help, we need to be open to allow those trials to change us. To make us better, not bitter.

"Now your attitudes and thoughts must all be constantly changing
for the better. Yes, you must be a new and different person."
(Ephesians 4:23, TLB)

Power to change

In the past, we have wanted to change and were unable to do so. We could not free ourselves from our hurts, hang-ups, or habits. In Principle 2, we come to understand that God's power can change us and our situation.

"For I can do everything God asks me to with the help of Christ who
gives me the strength and the power." (Philippians 4:13, TLB)

"Lead me; teach me; for you are the God who gives me salvation.
I have no hope except in you." (Psalm 25:5, TLB)

Expect to change

Remember you are only at the second principle. Don't quit before the miracle happens! With God's help, the changes that you have longed for are just *steps* away.

"I am sure that God who began the good work within you will keep
right on helping you grow in his grace until his task within you is

finally finished on that day when Jesus Christ returns."
(Philippians 1:6, TLB)

How do we find hope? By faith in our Higher Power, Jesus Christ.

*"Now faith is being sure of what we hope for and certain of what
we do not see." (Hebrews 11:1)*

Write About It

1. Before taking this step, where were you trying to find hope?

   Imposing my will...

2. What do you believe about God? What are some of His characteristics?

   I believe God has a plan that is more
   righteous and grandiose than I could ever conceive

   God is the best aspects of our character ... love, kindness,
   compassion, courage, endurance, honesty, integrity

3. How are your feelings for your heavenly Father and your earthly father alike? How do they differ?

Similarities : Respect, trust, honor, love
Provider

Differences : Unconditional acknowledgement of His wisdom, spiritual perfection, and unlimited power...

Gal 5:22

4. How can your relationship with your Higher Power, Jesus Christ, help you step out of your denial and face reality?

My unconditional love for Jesus Christ has inspired me to consider How the creator of the universe allowed Himself to be humiliated, tortured, and nailed to a tree... This selfless nature is something that is worthy of being emulated.

5. In what areas of your life are you now ready to let God help you?

Activities of focus:
• Helping my family in father, son, and daughter
• Finding a church in which I can contribute my talents
• Finding new friends
• Personal pride
• Personal lust

6. What things are you ready to change in your life? Where can you get the power to change them?

I have come to realize that the most important "things" in life are <u>not</u> things.

I believe that through daily prayer, study of Scripture, and a conscious effort to do the will of God will guide me on the path that I was meant to walk... helping others and glorifying God.

SANITY

Principle 2: Earnestly believe that God exists, that I matter to Him, and that He has the power to help me recover.

"Happy are those who mourn, for they shall be comforted."
(Matthew 5:4)

Step 2: We came to believe that a power greater than ourselves could restore us to sanity.

"For it is God who works in you to will and to act according to his good purpose." (Philippians 2:13)

Think About It

Insanity has been described as "doing the same thing over and over again, expecting a different result each time."

Sanity has been defined as "wholeness of mind; making decisions based on the truth."

The following are some of the gifts we will receive when we believe that our Higher Power, Jesus Christ, has the power and will restore us to SANITY!

Strength

Jesus gives us strength to face the fears that in the past have caused us to fight, flee, or freeze.

*"God is our refuge and our strength, an ever-present help in trouble.
Therefore we will not fear." (Psalm 46:1)*

*"My mind and my body may grow weak, but God is my strength;
he is all I ever need." (Psalm 73:26, GNB)*

Acceptance

We learn to have realistic expectations of ourselves and others.

*"Accept one another, then, for the glory of God,
as Christ has accepted you." (Romans 15:7, GNB)*

New life

We discover that we have an opportunity for a second chance! We do
not have to live by our old ways any longer.

*"When someone becomes a Christian he becomes a brand new
person inside. He is not the same anymore. A new life has begun!"
(2 Corinthians 5:17, TLB)*

(Eph 4: 22-24)

Integrity

We begin to follow through on our promises. Others start trusting
what we say.

*"Nothing brings me greater joy than hearing that my children
are living in the truth." (3 John 4, PH)*

Trust

We begin to trust relationships with others and our Higher Power,
Jesus Christ!

*"It is dangerous to be concerned with what others think of you,
but if you trust the LORD, you are safe." (Proverbs 29:25, GNB)*

(Prov 3: 5-6)

Your Higher Power, Jesus Christ, loves you just the way you are!

No matter what you have done in the past, God wants to forgive it!

"While we were still sinners, Christ died for us." (Romans 5:8) ✱

No matter what shape your life is in today, together God and you can handle it!

"And God is faithful; he will not let you be tempted beyond what you can bear. But <u>when you are tempted</u>, he will also <u>provide a way out.</u>" (1 Corinthians 10:13) ✳

And if you take action to complete the next principle, your future will be blessed and secure!

"So don't be anxious about tomorrow. God will take care of your tomorrow too. Live one day at a time." (Matthew 6:34, TLB)

" ... each day has enough trouble of its own."

Principle 2 Prayer

Dear God, <u>I have tried to "fix" and "control"</u> my life's <u>hurts, hung-ups, or habits all by myself.</u> I admit that, by myself, I am powerless to change. <u>I need to</u> begin to believe and <u>receive Your</u> power to help me recover. You loved me enough to send Your Son to the cross to die for my sins. Help me <u>be open to the hope that I can only find in Him.</u> Please help me to start living my life one day at a time. In Jesus' name I pray, Amen.

Write About It

1. What things have you been doing over and over again, expecting a different result each time (insanity)?

I have repeatedly tried to change people, situations, and things that were beyond my control in order to "make them better"... sometimes out of selfish intentions.

2. What is your definition of sanity? ⟹ ∴

Repeatedly doing things that in the past have caused problems... thinking that... "this time will be different" is ins

∴ Consciously doing the righteous thing we know will glorify God

Rom 3:21-25 The law of God is an expression of His charact

3. How have your past expectations of yourself or others been unrealistic? Give examples.

① Drinking alcohol... I have stopped drinking for as much as 2 years... thinking that I "have-it-under-control" I began drinking again and eventually got in trouble because of the effects alcohol has on my judgement.

② I have strayed from spirituality when I got into trouble... my thinking was that "I can change this situation with my own efforts

4. In the past, how has trusting only in your own feelings and emotions gotten you in trouble?

<u>Rationalization</u>: I have "reasoned" that because I have been successful in overcoming setbacks and adversity in the past in one type of situation ... I should be able to overcome another unrelated situation with my intellect, personality, and abilities

<u>Minimization</u>: I have consciously or subconsciously underestimated the true nature of a situation.

5. How can your Higher Power, Jesus Christ, help restore you to make sane decisions? How do you get a second chance?

Using prayer, reflection, and discernment...focus my efforts toward doing the next righteous thing ... even if it is the most difficult. Ask the question ...: "What would Jesus do "

Getting a second chance, I believe, comes with putting our set-backs, disappointments, and failures behind us without looking back. Be honest about our expectations and move forward with hope ☺

6. What areas of your life are you ready to release control of and hand over to God? Be specific.

PRINCIPLE 2 VERSES

"Remember that in the past you were without Christ. You were not citizens of Israel, and you had no part in the agreements with the promise that God made to his people. You had no hope, and you did not know God. But now in Christ Jesus, you who were far away from God are brought near through the blood of Christ's death."
(Ephesians 2:12–13, NCV)

"But this precious treasure—this light and power that now shine within us—is held in a perishable container, that is, in our weak bodies. Everyone can see that the glorious power within must be from God and is not our own. We are pressed on every side by troubles, but not crushed and broken. We are perplexed because we don't know why things happen as they do, but we don't give up and quit."
(2 Corinthians 4:7–8, TLB)

"And this is the secret: that Christ in your hearts is your only hope of glory." (Colossians 1:27, TLB)

"Don't copy the behavior and customs of this world, but be a new and different person with a fresh newness in all you do and think. Then you will learn from your own experience how his ways will really satisfy you." (Romans 12:2, TLB)

H
... be transformed by the renewal of your mind, that you may disern the will of God.

"He will not break the bruised reed, nor quench the dimly burning flame. He will encourage the fainthearted, those tempted to despair. He will see full justice given to all who have been wronged."
(Isaiah 42:3, TLB)

TURN

Principle 3: Consciously choose to commit all my life and will to Christ's care and control.

> *"Happy are the meek." (Matthew 5:5)*

Step 3: We made a decision to turn our lives and our wills over to the care of God.

> *"Therefore, I urge you, brothers, in view of God's mercy, to offer your bodies as living sacrifices, holy and pleasing to God— this is your spiritual act of worship." (Romans 12:1)*

Think About It

How do you TURN your life over to the one and only Higher Power, Jesus Christ?

Trust

Deciding to turn your life and your will over to God requires only trust. Trust is putting the faith you found in Principle 2 into action.

> *"If you declare with your lips, 'Jesus is Lord,' and believe in your heart that God raised him from the dead, you will be saved." (Romans 10:9, GNB)*

Understand

Relying solely on your own understanding got you into recovery in the first place! After you make the decision to ask Jesus into your life, you need to begin to seek His will for your life in all your decisions.

"Trust in the LORD with all your heart and lean not on your own understanding; in all your ways acknowledge him, and he will make your paths straight." (Proverbs 3:5–6)

Repent

To truly repent, you must not only *turn away* from your sins, but *turn toward* God. Repentance allows you to enjoy the freedom of your loving relationship with God.

"Turn from your sins and act on this glorious news!"
(Mark 1:15, TLB)

"Don't let the world around you squeeze you into its own mold, but let God remake you so that your whole attitude of mind is changed." (Romans 12:2, PH)

The law of God is an expression of His character

New life (God-Consciousness versus sin-consciousness)

After you ask Jesus into your heart, you will have a new life! You will no longer be bound to your old sin nature. God has declared you NOT GUILTY, and you no longer have to live under the power of sin!

"Now God says he will accept and acquit us—declare us 'not guilty'—if we trust Jesus Christ to take away our sins." (Romans 3:22, TLB)

We will work on the "how tos" of TURNING our life and will over to God in Lesson 6. But do not forget this key point:

Turning your life over to Christ is a once-in-a-lifetime commitment!
Turning your will over to Him requires a daily *recommitment*!
Pray the following prayer daily.

Principle 3 Prayer

Dear God, I have tried to do it all by myself, on my own power, and I have failed. Today, I want to turn my life over to You. I ask You to be my Lord and my Savior. You are the One and only Higher Power! I ask that You help me start to think less about me and my will. I want to daily turn my will over to You, to daily seek Your direction and wisdom for my life. Please continue to help me overcome my hurts, hang-ups, and habits and may that victory over them help others as they see Your power at work in changing my life. Help me to do Your will always. In Jesus' name I pray, Amen.

Write About It

1. What is stopping you from asking Jesus Christ into your heart as your Lord and Savior? (If you have already asked Christ into your life, describe your experience.) I have asked Jesus to come into my ♡....

   One evening while meditating and in-prayer I made a conscious decision to invite and receive Jesus into my life so that I could begin to know Him more personally...

   In doing so I experienced a change in "attitude"... I felt a release of my intellectuality of being "in-control" and began to trust Jesus to transform my mind, spirit, and soul to emulate His character... ☺ ♱

2. How has relying on your "own understanding" caused problems in your life? Be specific.

   Relying on my own understanding has caused problems in every aspect of my life i.e. family, friends, and work. In fact, many times my efforts to change situations or others were done-so with the best of intentions ... to change others minds while doing so I often times alienated others, made some situations worse, and came away with arguments and frustrations.

3. What does "repent" mean to you? What do you need to repent of?

To me "repentence" means to willfully and consciously turn to God from "self" unconditionally and with no residual guilt or apprehension.

4. What does the declaration of "not guilty" found in Romans 3:22 mean to you? God's benevolent, merciful, and loving nature is a gift provided to all who receive and are faithful to Jesus Christ ... irregardless of past transgressio

Rom 8 11-$1;

Eph 4: 31-32;

5. When you turn your life over to your Higher Power, Jesus Christ, you have a "new life" (see 2 Corinthians 5:17). What does that "new life" mean to you?

6. What does the Principle 3 prayer mean to you?

ACTION

Principle 3: Consciously choose to commit all my life and will to Christ's care and control.

men of strong character

"Happy are the meek." (Matthew 5:5)

Step 3: We made a decision to turn our lives and our wills over to the care of God.

"Therefore, I urge you, brothers, in view of God's mercy, to offer your bodies as living sacrifices, holy and pleasing to God— this is your spiritual act of worship." (Romans 12:1)

Think About It

Even after taking the first two steps we can still be stuck in the cycle of failure: guilt ➪ anger ➪ fear ➪ depression! – – – ⇢ Death

How do we get "unstuck"? How do we get past the barriers of pride, fear, guilt, worry, and doubt that keep us from taking this step?

The answer is *we need to take ACTION!*

Accept Jesus Christ as your Higher Power and Savior!

Make the decision to ask Jesus into your heart. Now is the time to commit your life, to establish that personal relationship with Jesus that He so desires.

"If you confess with your mouth, 'Jesus is Lord,' and believe in your
heart that God raised him from the dead, you will be saved."
(Romans 10:9)

Commit to seek and follow HIS will!

We need to change our definition of willpower: Willpower is the willingness to accept God's power. We see that there is no room for God if we are full of ourselves.

"Teach me to do your will, for you are my God; may your good
Spirit lead me on level ground." (Psalm 143:9–10)

1. Come and receive Salvation
2. Learn in Discipleship
3. Serve others righteously (obedience to His word)

Turn it over

"Let go; let God!" Turn over all the big things and the little things in your life to your Higher Power. Jesus Christ wants a relationship with *ALL* of you. What burdens are you carrying that you want to *TURN OVER* to God?

3. Instruction under discipline

"Come to me and I will give you rest—all of you who work so hard
beneath a heavy yoke. Wear my yoke for it fits perfectly and let
me teach you; for I am gentle and humble, and you shall find rest
for your souls." (Matthew 11:28–30, TLB)

It's only the beginning

In the third principle we make only the initial decision, the commitment to seek and follow God's will. Our walk with our Higher Power, Jesus Christ, begins with this decision and is followed by a lifelong process of growing as a Christian.

"God who began the good work within you will keep right on help-
ing you grow in his grace until his task within is finally finished."
(Philippians 1:6, TLB)

One day at a time

Recovery happens one day at a time. If we remain stuck in the yesterday or constantly worry about tomorrow, we will waste the precious time of the present. We can only change our hurts, hang-ups, and habits in the present.

"So don't be anxious about tomorrow. God will take care of your tomorrow too. Live one day at a time." (Matthew 6:34, TLB)

Next: How do I ask Christ into my life?

Ask yourself the following four questions (see box), and if you answer yes to all of them, pray the prayer that follows them. That's it. That's all you have to do!

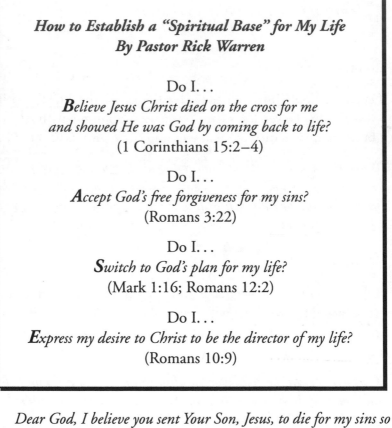

How to Establish a "Spiritual Base" for My Life
By Pastor Rick Warren

Do I...
B*elieve Jesus Christ died on the cross for me and showed He was God by coming back to life?*
(1 Corinthians 15:2–4)

Do I...
A*ccept God's free forgiveness for my sins?*
(Romans 3:22)

Do I...
S*witch to God's plan for my life?*
(Mark 1:16; Romans 12:2)

Do I...
E*xpress my desire to Christ to be the director of my life?*
(Romans 10:9)

Dear God, I believe you sent Your Son, Jesus, to die for my sins so I can be forgiven. I'm sorry for my sins and I want to live the rest of my life the way you want me to. Please put Your Spirit in my life to direct me. Amen.

Write About It

1. What differences have you noticed in your life now that you have accepted Jesus Christ as your Higher Power?

   A. I see "good" in people and have become more patient and open-minded with others

   B. I have become more humble, kind, gentle and accepting of the sometimes frustrating things

2. How has your definition of willpower changed since you have been in recovery?

   "Will-power" has been transformed from my conscious effort to impose "my-will" on things to accepting the people, places, and things as incremental components to God's master plan.

3. What have you been able to turn over to God?

   1. My ex-wife's deliberate attempts to undermine my relationship(s) with my kids

   2. My frustration in the length of my incarceration

   3. My concerns on what the future will hold for me after my release.

4. What do you fear turning over to His care?

5. What is keeping you from turning them over?

6. What does the phrase "live one day at a time" mean to you?

1 Peter 4:1

Living in the present with a determination to be a kind, gentle, and helpful person. Accepting things that are hurtful or painful with an attitude of "this too shall pass," and also accepting non-ideal situations as a "test" to my mettle and character.

7. What is a major concern in your life?

8. What's stopping you from turning it over to your Higher Power, Jesus Christ?

Principle 3 Verses

"If you confess with your mouth, 'Jesus is Lord,' and believe in your heart that God raised him from the dead, you will be saved."
(Romans 10:9)

"If you had faith even as small as a tiny mustard seed you could say to this mountain, 'Move!' and it would go far away. Nothing would be impossible." (Matthew 17:20, TLB)

"Come to me and I will give you rest—all of you who work so hard beneath a heavy yoke. Wear my yoke—for it fits perfectly—and let me teach you; for I am gentle and humble, and you shall find rest for your souls; for I give you only light burdens."
(Matthew 11:28–30, TLB)

"Commit everything you do to the Lord. Trust him to help you do it and he will." (Psalm 37:5, TLB)

"Lead me; teach me; for you are the God who gives me salvation. I have no hope except in you." (Psalm 25:5, TLB)

"Indeed, in our hearts we felt the sentence of death. But this happened that we might not rely on ourselves but on God, who raises the dead." (2 Corinthians 1:9)

"Teach me to do your will, for you are my God; may your good Spirit lead me on level ground." (Psalm 143:10)

"In everything you do, put God first, and he will direct you and crown your efforts with success." (Proverbs 3:6, TLB)

AFTERWORD

Now that you have completed all six lessons in this guide to the best of your ability, CONGRATULATIONS are most definitely in order!

In Principle 1 you faced your denial and admitted that by yourself you were powerless to manage your addictive or compulsive behavior.

*"I know that nothing good lives in me, that is, in my sinful nature.
For I have the desire to do what is good, but I cannot carry it out."
(Romans 7:18)*

In Principle 2 you found the hope that God could and would restore you to sanity, and that only He could provide the power for you to recover.

*"For God is at work within you, helping you want to obey him, and
then helping you do what he wants." (Philippians 2:13, TLB)*

And finally, in Principle 3, you were able to take the action, to make the decision to turn your life and your will over to God's care and direction.

*"And so, dear brothers, I plead with you to give your bodies to God.
Let them be a living sacrifice, holy—the kind he can accept. When
you think of what he has done for you, is that too much to ask?
(Romans 12:1, TLB)*

Now, you are ready to take the next step in your journey on the "Road to Recovery." The next participant's guide deals with facing your past—the good and the bad. Principle 4 can be difficult, but remember you're not going to go through it alone. Your Higher Power, Jesus Christ, and others that He has placed alongside you on your "Road to Recovery" will be with you every step of the way.

CELEBRATE RECOVERY®
CREED

On the road to recovery we are changed when we accept
God's grace and forgiveness to solve our life problems.

We are changed when we become willing to share
our experience, strength and hope with one another.

Each of us needs repentance and recovery to live life
the way God intended.

We need fellowship and accountability to help us grow spiritually.

We utilize biblical truth that we need each other to grow
spiritually and emotionally.

By working the eight recovery principles we maintain
freedom from our life's hurts, habits and hang-ups.

This freedom creates peace, serenity, joy and most importantly,
a stronger personal relationship with our loving
and forgiving Higher Power, Jesus Christ!

Written by the brothers from the Celebrate Recovery ministry in
Sierra Conservation Center in Jamestown, California

Celebrate Recovery®

Taking an Honest and Spiritual Inventory

PARTICIPANT'S GUIDE 2

John Baker is the founder of Celebrate Recovery®, a ministry born out of the heart of Saddleback Church. Over the last fourteen years, more than 7,500 individuals have gone through this Christ-centered recovery program at Saddleback. The Celebrate Recovery program is now being used in thousands of churches nationwide. In 1993, John and Pastor Rick Warren wrote the Celebrate Recovery curriculum which has been published and translated into several languages.

John began serving at Saddleback as a lay pastor in 1991. In 1992, he was asked to join the Saddleback Church staff as the Director of Small Groups and Recovery. In 1995, his responsibilities increased as he became the Pastor of Membership. In this position, John's responsibilities included pastoral counseling, pastoral care, Celebrate Recovery, support groups, small groups, and family, singles, and recreation ministries. In 1996, he oversaw the development of Saddleback's lay counseling ministry.

In June 1997, John became the Pastor of Ministries, responsible for the recruitment, training, and deployment of church members to serve in one of the more than 156 different ministries at Saddleback.

In 2001, Rick Warren asked John to become the Pastor of Celebrate Recovery. This is John's shape, his passion, and his calling. In addition, he is part of Saddleback's Purpose Driven team. John is a nationally known speaker and trainer in helping churches start Celebrate Recovery ministries. These ministries, in thousands of churches, reach out not only to their congregations but also to their communities in helping those dealing with a hurt, hang-up, or habit.

John and his wife Cheryl have been married thirty-five years and have served together in Celebrate Recovery since 1991. They have two adult children, Laura and Johnny. In 2004, Johnny and his wife, Jeni, gave John and Cheryl their first grandchild, Maggie.

UPDATED EDITION

Celebrate Recovery®

Taking an Honest and Spiritual Inventory

Participant's Guide 2

A recovery program based on
eight principles from the Beatitudes

JOHN BAKER

FOREWORD BY RICK WARREN

ZONDERVAN™

GRAND RAPIDS, MICHIGAN 49530 USA

CONTENTS

FOREWORD BY RICK WARREN

You've undoubtedly heard the expression "Time heals all wounds." Unfortunately, it isn't true. As a pastor I frequently talk with people who are still carrying hurts from thirty or forty years ago. The truth is, time often makes things worse. Wounds that are left untended fester and spread infection throughout your entire body. Time only extends the pain if the problem isn't dealt with.

Celebrate Recovery® is a biblical and balanced program that can help you overcome your hurts, habits, and hang-ups. Based on the actual words of Jesus rather than psychological theory, this recovery program is more effective in helping people change than anything else I've seen or heard of. Over the years I've witnessed how the Holy Spirit has used this program to transform literally thousands of lives at Saddleback Church and help people grow toward full Christlike maturity.

Perhaps you are familiar with the classic 12-Step program of AA and other groups. While undoubtedly many lives have been helped through the 12 Steps, I've always been uncomfortable with that program's vagueness about the nature of God, the saving power of Jesus Christ, and the ministry of the Holy Spirit. So I began an intense study of the Scriptures to discover what God had to say about "recovery." To my amazement, I found the principles of recovery—in their logical order—given by Christ in His most famous message, the Sermon on the Mount.

My study resulted in a ten-week series of messages called "The Road to Recovery." During that series my associate pastor John Baker developed the four participant's guides, which became the heart of our Celebrate Recovery program.

As you work through these participant's guides, I trust that you will come to realize many benefits from this program. Most of all, however, my prayer for you is that, through Celebrate Recovery, you will find deep peace and lasting freedom in Jesus Christ as you walk your own road to recovery.

Dr. Rick Warren
Senior Pastor, Saddleback Church

INTRODUCTION

The purpose of Celebrate Recovery® is to allow us to become free from life's hurts, hang-ups, and habits. By working through the eight principles of recovery based on the Beatitudes, with Jesus Christ as our Higher Power, we can and will change! We will begin to experience the true peace and serenity that we have been seeking. We will no longer need to rely on our dysfunctional, compulsive, and addictive behaviors as a temporary "fix" for our pain.

By applying the biblical principles of conviction, conversion, surrender, confession, restitution, prayer, quiet time, witnessing, and helping one another found within the eight principles, we will restore or develop stronger relationships with others and God.

You have completed the first three principles to the best of your ability: you have "gotten right with God." Now as you prepare to work Principle 4, you begin the journey of "getting right with yourself" (Principles 4–5).

After each lesson, there is an exercise for you to complete. Answer each question to the best of your ability. Don't worry about what you think the answer *should* be. Pray and then write down the answer from your heart. Remember John 8:32: "Then you will know the truth, and the truth will set you free."

An important word of caution: Do not begin this principle without a sponsor or a strong accountability partner (these are explained in Lesson 8)! You need someone you trust to help keep you balanced during this step, not to do the work for you. Nobody can do that except you. But you need encouragement from someone who will support your progress and keep you accountable. That's what this program is all about.

After you have completed the exercise, share it with someone that you trust. Your group, an accountability partner, your sponsor or a close friend in recovery are all safe choices. You do not recover from your hurts, hang-ups, and habits from just attending recovery meetings. You must work and live the principles!

In His steps,
John Baker

THE ROAD TO RECOVERY

Eight Principles Based on the Beatitudes

By Pastor Rick Warren

1. **R**ealize I'm not God. I admit that I am powerless to control my tendency to do the wrong thing and that my life is unmanageable.
   "Happy are those who know they are spiritually poor."
   (Matthew 5:3)

2. **E**arnestly believe that God exists, that I matter to Him, and that He has the power to help me recover.
   "Happy are those who mourn, for they shall be comforted."
   (Matthew 5:4)

3. **C**onsciously choose to commit all my life and will to Christ's care and control.
   "Happy are the meek." (Matthew 5:5)

4. **O**penly examine and confess my faults to myself, to God, and to someone I trust.
   "Happy are the pure in heart." (Matthew 5:8)

5. **V**oluntarily submit to every change God wants to make in my life and humbly ask Him to remove my character defects.
   "Happy are those whose greatest desire is to do what God requires."
   (Matthew 5:6)

6. **E**valuate all my relationships. Offer forgiveness to those who have hurt me and make amends for harm I've done to others, except when to do so would harm them or others.
   "Happy are the merciful." (Matthew 5:7)
   "Happy are the peacemakers." (Matthew 5:9)

7. **R**eserve a daily time with God for self-examination, Bible reading, and prayer in order to know God and His will for my life and to gain the power to follow His will.

8. **Y**ield myself to God to be used to bring this Good News to others, both by my example and by my words.
   "Happy are those who are persecuted because they
   do what God requires." (Matthew 5:10)

Twelve Steps and
Their Biblical Comparisons

1. We admitted we were powerless over our addictions and compulsive behaviors, that our lives had become unmanageable.

   "I know that nothing good lives in me, that is, in my sinful nature. For I have the desire to do what is good, but I cannot carry it out." *(Romans 7:18)*

2. We came to believe that a power greater than ourselves could restore us to sanity.

   "For it is God who works in you to will and to act according to his good purpose." (Philippians 2:13)

3. We made a decision to turn our lives and our wills over to the care of God.

   "Therefore, I urge you, brothers, in view of God's mercy, to offer your bodies as living sacrifices, holy and pleasing to God— this is your spiritual act of worship." (Romans 12:1)

4. We made a searching and fearless moral inventory of ourselves.

   "Let us examine our ways and test them, and let us return to the LORD." (Lamentations 3:40)

5. We admitted to God, to ourselves, and to another human being the exact nature of our wrongs.

   "Therefore confess your sins to each other and pray for each other so that you may be healed." (James 5:16)

6. We were entirely ready to have God remove all these defects of character.

   "Humble yourselves before the Lord, and he will lift you up." (James 4:10)

7. We humbly asked Him to remove all our shortcomings.

> *"If we confess our sins, he is faithful and just and will forgive us our sins and purify us from all unrighteousness." (1 John 1:9)*

8. We made a list of all persons we had harmed and became willing to make amends to them all.

> *"Do to others as you would have them do to you." (Luke 6:31)*

9. We made direct amends to such people whenever possible, except when to do so would injure them or others.

> *"Therefore, if you are offering your gift at the altar and there remember that your brother has something against you, leave your gift there in front of the altar. First go and be reconciled to your brother; then come and offer your gift." (Matthew 5:23–24)*

10. We continued to take personal inventory and when we were wrong, promptly admitted it.

> *"So, if you think you are standing firm, be careful that you don't fall!" (1 Corinthians 10:12)*

11. We sought through prayer and meditation to improve our conscious contact with God, praying only for knowledge of His will for us and power to carry that out.

> *"Let the word of Christ dwell in you richly." (Colossians 3:16)*

12. Having had a spiritual experience as the result of these steps, we try to carry this message to others and to practice these principles in all our affairs.

> *"Brothers, if someone is caught in a sin, you who are spiritual should restore him gently. But watch yourself, or you also may be tempted." (Galatians 6:1)*

Serenity Prayer

If you have attended secular recovery programs, you have seen the first four lines of the "Prayer for Serenity." The following is the complete prayer. I encourage you to pray it daily as you work through the principles!

Prayer for Serenity

God, grant me the serenity
to accept the things I cannot change,
the courage to change the things I can,
and the wisdom to know the difference.
Living one day at a time,
enjoying one moment at a time;
accepting hardship as a pathway to peace;
taking, as Jesus did,
this sinful world as it is,
not as I would have it;
trusting that You will make all things right
if I surrender to Your will;
so that I may be reasonably happy in this life
and supremely happy with You forever in the next.
Amen.

Reinhold Niebuhr

CELEBRATE RECOVERY'S SMALL GROUP GUIDELINES

The following five guidelines will ensure that your small group is a safe place. They need to be read at the beginning of every meeting.

1. Keep your sharing focused on your own thoughts and feelings. Limit your sharing to three to five minutes.
2. There is NO cross talk. Cross talk is when two individuals engage in conversation excluding all others. Each person is free to express his or her feelings without interruptions.
3. We are here to support one another, not "fix" another.
4. Anonymity and confidentiality are basic requirements. What is shared in the group stays in the group. The only exception is when someone threatens to injure themselves or others.
5. Offensive language has no place in a Christ-centered recovery group.

(HONESTY)
MORAL

Principle 4: Openly examine and confess my faults to myself, to God, and to someone I trust.

"Happy are the pure in heart." (Matthew 5:8)

Step 4: We made a searching and fearless moral inventory of ourselves.

"Let us examine our ways and test them, and let us return to the LORD." (Lamentations 3:40)

> **An important word of caution:** Do not begin this principle without a sponsor or a strong accountability partner (these are explained in Lesson 8)! You need someone you trust to help keep you balanced during this step, not to do the work for you. Nobody can do that except you. But you need encouragement from someone who will support your progress and hold you accountable. That's what this program is all about.

Think About It

In this principle, you need to list (inventory) all the significant events—good and bad—in your life. You need to be as honest as you can be to allow God to show you your part and how that affected you and others. The acrostic for MORAL shows you how to begin.

Mind (Worldview): What I think/believe
Heart (Intuition): What I feel/love
Strength (Actions): My behavior & Physicality
Soul (God Aspect): My moral & spiritual devotion to truth

Make time

Set aside a special time to begin your inventory. Schedule an appointment with yourself. Set aside a day or a weekend to get alone with God! Clear your mind of the present hassles of daily life.

"Then listen to me. Keep silence and I will teach you wisdom!"
(Job 33:33, TLB)

Open

Open your heart and your mind to allow the feelings that the pain of the past has blocked or caused you to deny. Try to "wake up" your feelings! Ask yourself, "What do I feel guilty about? What do I resent? What do I fear? Am I trapped in self-pity, alibis, and dishonest thinking?"

"Let me express my anguish. Let me be free to speak out
of the bitterness of my soul." (Job 7:11, TLB)

Rely

Rely on Jesus, your Higher Power, to give you the courage and strength this exercise requires.

"Love the Lord, all of you who are his people; for the Lord
protects those who are loyal to him. . . . So cheer up! Take courage
if you are depending on the Lord." (Psalm 31:23–24, TLB)

Analyze

Analyze your past honestly. To do a "searching and fearless moral inventory," you must step out of your denial!

That's all that the word *moral* means—honest! This step requires looking through your denial of the past into the truth!

"The Lord gave us mind and conscience;
we cannot hide from ourselves." (Proverbs 20:27, GNB)

List

List both the good and the bad. Keep your inventory balanced! If you just look at all the bad things of your past, you will distort your inventory and open yourself to unnecessary pain.

successes

"Let us examine our ways and test them." (Lamentations 3:40) Conform to His Will

Learn from our mistakes, trust God and be willing to change. →

The verse doesn't say, "Examine only your bad, negative ways." You need to honestly focus on the pros *and* the cons of your past!

As you compile your inventory, you will find that you have done some harmful things to yourself and others. No one's inventory (life) is flawless. We have all "missed the mark" in some area of our lives. In recovery we are not to dwell on the past, but we need to understand it so we can begin to allow God to change us. Jesus told us, "My purpose is to give life in all its fullness" (John 10:10, TLB).

Principle 4 Prayer

Dear God, You know my past, all the good and the bad things that I've done. In this step, I ask that You give me the strength and the courage to list those things so that I can "come clean" and face them and the truth. Please help me reach out to others You have placed along my "road to recovery." Thank You for providing them to help me keep balanced as I do my inventory. In Christ's name I pray, Amen.

Write About It

1. Where will you go for quiet time to begin your inventory?

2. What date have you set aside to start? What time?

3. What are your fears as you begin your inventory? Why?

4. What can you do to help you "wake up" your feelings?

5. Describe your experience of turning your life over to Christ.

6. How do you attempt to turn over your will to God's care on a daily basis?

7. List the things you have used to block the pain of your past.

8. What have you done to step out of your denial?

9. How can you continue to find new ways out of your denial of the past?

10. Why is it important to do a written inventory?

11. What are some of the good things you have done in the past?

12. What are some of the negative things you have done in the past?

13. Do you have a sponsor or accountability partner to help you keep your inventory balanced?

SPONSOR

Principle 4: Openly examine and confess my faults to myself, to God, and to someone I trust.

"Happy are the pure in heart." (Matthew 5:8)

Step 4: We made a searching and fearless moral inventory of ourselves.

"Let us examine our ways and test them, and let us return to the LORD." (Lamentations 3:40)

Think About It

You've heard the word "sponsor" for a few weeks now. I'm sure you have at least a vague idea of what a sponsor is, but maybe you're wondering why you even need one.

<u>W</u>hy do I need a sponsor and/or an accountability partner?

There are three reasons why having a sponsor is vital.

Having a sponsor and/or accountability partner is biblical.

"Two are better off than one, because together they can work more effectively. If one of them falls down, the other can help him up. But if someone is alone . . . there is no one to help him. . . . Two men can resist an attack that would defeat one man alone."
(Ecclesiastes 4:9–12, GNB)

"As iron sharpens iron, one man sharpens another."
(Proverbs 27:17)

Having a sponsor and/or accountability partner is a key part of your recovery program.

Your recovery program has four key elements to success:

- To the best of your ability, maintain your **honest** view of reality as you *work* each principle. The best way to ensure this is to have a sponsor and develop a strong accountability support team.
- Make recovery group **meetings** a priority in your schedule. Knowing that a sponsor or accountability partner will be there to greet you or notice that you're not there is an added incentive to attend.
- Maintain your **spiritual program** with Jesus Christ, through prayer, meditation, and studying His Word.
- Get involved in **service**, which includes serving as a sponsor (after you have completed all eight principles) or accountability partner.

Having a sponsor and/or an accountability partner is the best guard against relapse.

By providing feedback to keep you on track, a sponsor and/or accountability partner can see your old dysfunctional hurts, hang-ups, and habits beginning to return, and point them out to you quickly. He or she can confront you with truth and love without placing shame or guilt.

What are the qualities of a sponsor?

"Though good advice lies deep within a counselor's heart, the wise man will draw it out." (Proverbs 20:5, TLB)

When you are selecting a possible sponsor, look for the following qualities:

1. Does his walk match his talk? Is he living by the eight principles?
2. Does she have a growing relationship with Jesus Christ?
3. Does he express the desire to help others on the "road to recovery?"
4. Does she show compassion, care, and hope, but not pity?

5. Is he a good listener?
6. Is she strong enough to confront your denial or procrastination?
7. Does he offer suggestions?
8. Can she share her own current struggles with others?

What is the role of a sponsor?

1. She can be there to discuss issues in detail that are too personal or would take too much time in a meeting.
2. He is available in times of crisis or potential relapse.
3. She serves as a sounding board by providing an objective point of view.
4. He is there to encourage you to work the principles at your own speed. He does not work the steps for you!
5. Most important, she attempts to model the lifestyle resulting from working the eight principles.
6. A sponsor can resign or can be fired.

How do I find a sponsor and/or an accountability partner?

First, your sponsor or accountability partner MUST be of the same sex as you. After you have narrowed the field down with that requirement, listen to people share. Do you relate to or resonate with what is spoken? Ask others in your group to go out for coffee after the meeting. Get to know the person before you ask him or her to be your sponsor or accountability partner!

If you ask someone to be your sponsor or accountability partner and that person says no, do not take it as a personal rejection. Ask someone else. You can even ask for a "temporary" sponsor or accountability partner.

Ask God to lead you to the sponsor and/or accountability partner of His choosing. He already has someone in mind for you.

What is the difference between a sponsor and an accountability partner?

A sponsor is someone who has completed the four participant's guides. He or she has worked through the eight principles and the 12 Steps. The main goal of this relationship is to choose someone to guide you through the program.

An accountability partner is someone you ask to hold you accountable for certain areas of your recovery or issues, such as meeting attendance, journaling, and so forth. This person can be at the same level of recovery as you are, unlike a sponsor, who should have completed the eight principles or 12 Steps. The main goal of this relationship is to encourage one another. You can even form an accountability team of three or four.

The accountability partner or group acts as the "team," whereas the sponsor's role is that of a "coach."

Write About It

1. Why is it important for you to have a support team?

2. What qualities are you looking for in a sponsor?

3. How have you attempted to find a sponsor/accountability partner?

4. What are some new places and ways you can try to find a sponsor/accountability partner?

5. What is the difference between a sponsor and an accountability partner?

6. List the names and phone numbers of possible sponsors or accountability partners. These should be individuals you have met on your "Road to Recovery" who have touched you in the sharing of their experiences, strengths, and hopes.

INVENTORY

Principle 4: Openly examine and confess my faults to myself, to God, and to someone I trust.

"Happy are the pure in heart." (Matthew 5:8)

Step 4: We made a searching and fearless moral inventory of ourselves.

"Let us examine our ways and test them, and let us return to the LORD." (Lamentations 3:40)

Think About It

Now that you have the background information and you've built your accountability team, it's time to start writing your inventory. This lesson will provide you with the tools you need.

How do I start my inventory?

The Celebrate Recovery Inventory is divided into five sections. It will help you keep focused on reality and recall events that you may have repressed. Remember, you are not going through this alone. You are developing your support team to guide you, but even more important, you are growing in your relationship with Jesus Christ!

It will take you more than one page to write out your inventory. You have permission to copy the "Celebrate Recovery Principle 4 Inventory Worksheet" on pages 30 and 31.

Column 1: "The Person"

In this column you list the person or object you resent or fear. Go as far back as you can. Resentment is mostly unexpressed anger and fear.

> *"Get rid of all bitterness, rage and anger, brawling and slander, along with every form of malice." (Ephesians 4:31)*

Column 2: "The Cause"

It has been said that "hurt people hurt people." In this column you are going to list the specific actions that someone did to hurt you. What did the person do to cause you resentment and/or fear? An example would be the alcoholic father who was emotionally unavailable for you as you were growing up. Another example would be the parent who attempted to control and dominate your life. This reflective look can be very painful. But . . .

> *"Fear not, for I am with you. Do not be dismayed. I am your God. I will strengthen you; I will help you; I will uphold you with my victorious right hand." (Isaiah 41:10, TLB)*

Column 3: "The Effect"

In this column write down how that specific hurtful action affected your life. List the effects it had on your past and your present.

Column 4: "The Damage"

Which of your basic instincts were injured?
Social—broken relationships, slander
Security—physical safety, financial loss
Sexual—abusive relationships, damaged intimacy
No matter how you have been hurt, no matter how lost you may feel, God wants to comfort and restore you.

> *"I will look for those that are lost, I bring back those that wander off, bandage those that are hurt, and heal those that are sick." (Ezekiel 34:16, GNB)*

Column 5: "My Part"

You need to ask yourself, "What part of my resentment against another is my responsibility?" Ask God to show you your part in a broken or damaged marriage or relationship, with a distant child or parent, or maybe a lost job. In addition, list all the people whom you have hurt and how you hurt them.

> *"Examine me, O God, and know my mind; test me, and discover . . .*
> *if there is any evil in me and guide me in the everlasting way."*
> *(Psalm 139:23–24)*

Please note: If you have been in an abusive relationship, especially as a small child, you can find great freedom in this part of the inventory. You see that you had **NO** part, **NO** responsibility for the cause of the resentment. By simply writing the words "none" or "not guilty" in column 5, you can begin to be free from the misplaced shame and guilt you have carried with you.

Celebrate Recovery has rewritten Step 4 for those who have been sexually or physically abused:

Made a searching and fearless moral inventory of ourselves, realizing all wrongs can be forgiven. Renounce the lie that the abuse was our fault.

More tools

1. Memorize Isaiah 1:18 (TLB): "Come, let's talk this over! says the Lord; no matter how deep the stain of your sins, I can take it out and make you as clean as freshly fallen snow. Even if you are stained as red as crimson, I can make you white as wool!"
2. Read the Principle 4 "Balancing the Scale" verses on page 29.
3. Keep your inventory balanced. List both the good and the bad! This is very important! As God reveals the good things that you have done in the past, or are doing in the present, list them on the reverse side of your copies of the "Celebrate Recovery Principle 4 Inventory Worksheet."
4. Continue to develop your support team.
5. Pray continuously.

Principle 4 Verses

Balancing the Scale

Emotion	Positive Scripture
Helplessness	*"For God is at work within you, helping you to want to obey him, and then helping you do what he wants." (Philippians 2:13, TLB)*
Dwelling on the past	*"When someone becomes a Christian he becomes a brand new person inside. He is not the same any more. A new life has begun!" (2 Corinthians 5:17, TLB)*
Wanting	*"And it is he who will supply all your needs from his riches in glory, because of what Christ Jesus has done for us." (Philippians 4:19, TLB)*
Loneliness	*Jesus says, "I am with you always." (Matthew 28:20, TLB)*
Oppression, Trouble	*"All who are oppressed may come to him. He is a refuge for them in their times of trouble." (Psalm 9:9, TLB)*
Fear, Doubt	*"Yes, be bold and strong! Banish fear and doubt! For remember, the Lord your God is with you wherever you go." (Joshua 1:9, TLB)*
Melancholy, Apathy	*"This is the day the Lord has made. We will rejoice and be glad in it." (Psalm 118:24, TLB)*
Worry	*"Let him have all your worries and cares, for he is always thinking about you and watching everything that concerns you." (1 Peter 5:7, TLB)*

CELEBRATE RECOVERY
PRINCIPLE 4 INVENTORY WORKSHEET

1. The Person	2. The Cause	3. The Effect
Who is the object of my resentment or fear?	What specific action did that person take that hurt me?	What effect did that action have on my life?

"Let us examine our ways and test them, and let us return to the Lord." (Lamentations 3:40)

4. The Damage	5. My Part
What damage did that action do to my basic social, security, and/or sexual instincts?	What part of the resentment am I responsible for?
	Who are the people I have hurt?
	How have I hurt them?

SPIRITUAL INVENTORY PART 1

⟿

Principle 4: Openly examine and confess my faults to myself, to God, and to someone I trust.

"Happy are the pure in heart." (Matthew 5:8)

Step 4: We made a searching and fearless moral inventory of ourselves.

"Let us examine our ways and test them, and let us return to the LORD." (Lamentations 3:40)

⟿

Think About It

"Search me, O God, and know my heart: test my thoughts. Point out anything you find in me that makes you sad, and lead me along the path of everlasting life." (Psalm 139:23–24, TLB)

The following list gives some of our additional shortcomings (sins) that can prevent God from working effectively in our lives. Reading through it and searching your heart will help you get started on your inventory!

Relationship with others

> *"Forgive us our sins, just as we have forgiven those who have sinned against us. Don't bring us into temptation, but deliver us from the Evil One." (Matthew 6:12–13, TLB)*

- Who has hurt you?
- Against whom have you been holding a grudge?
- Against whom are you seeking revenge?
- Are you jealous of someone else?

(Note: The people who you name in these areas will go in column 1 of your Celebrate Recovery Principle 4 Inventory Worksheet.)

- Who have you hurt?
- Who have you criticized or gossiped about?
- Have you justified your bad attitude by saying it is "their" fault?

(Note: The people who you name in these areas will go in column 5 of your Celebrate Recovery Principle 4 Inventory Worksheet.)

Priorities in life

> *"He will give them to you if you give him first place in your life and live as he wants you to." (Matthew 6:33, TLB)*

- After accepting Jesus Christ, in what areas of your life are you still not putting God first?
- What in your past is interfering with you doing God's will? Your ambition? Pleasures? Job? Hobbies? Money? Friendships? Personal goals?

Attitude

> *"Get rid of all bitterness, passion, and anger. No more shouting or insults. No more hateful feelings of any sort." (Ephesians 4:31, GNB)*

- Have you always complained about your circumstances?
- In what areas of your life are you ungrateful?
- Have you gotten angry and easily blown up at people?
- Have you been sarcastic?
- What in your past is causing you fear or anxiety?

Integrity

"Do not lie to each other. You have left your old sinful life and the things you did before." (Colossians 3:9, NCV)

- In what past dealing were you dishonest?
- Have you stolen things?
- Have you exaggerated to make yourself look better?
- In what areas of your past have you used false humility?
- Have you lived one way in front of your Christian friends and another way at home or at work?

Have you memorized Isaiah 1:18 (TLB) yet?

"Come, let's talk this over! says the Lord; no matter how deep the stain of your sins, I can take it out and make you as clean as freshly fallen snow. Even if you are stained as red as crimson, I can make you white as wool!"

Write About It

1. Relationship with Others

   - Who has hurt you? (Go as far back as you can). How did they specifically hurt you?

- Who are you holding a grudge against? (Seeking revenge?)

- Who are you jealous of? (Past and present.) Why?

- Who have you hurt? And how did you hurt them?

- Who have you been critical of or gossiped about? Why?

- How have you attempted to place the blame on someone else? (Be specific).

- What new healthy relationships have you developed since you have been in recovery?

2. Priorities in Life

   - What areas of your life have you been able to turn over to your Higher Power, Jesus Christ?

   - After acting on Principle 3, in what areas of your life are you still not putting God first? Why not?

   - What in your past is keeping you from seeking and following God's will for your life?

- Number the following list in order of your personal priorities.

  _____ career

  _____ family

  _____ church

  _____ Christ

  _____ friendships

  _____ money

  _____ ministry

- What are your personal goals for the next ninety days? (Keep it simple!)

3. Attitude

  - What areas in your life are you thankful for?

  - In the past, what things have you been ungrateful over?

- What causes you to lose your temper?

- To whom have you been sarcastic to in the past? (Give examples).

- What in your past are you still worried about?

- How has your attitude improved since you have been in recovery?

4. Integrity

- In the past, how have you exaggerated to make yourself look good? (Give examples.)

- Does your walk as a Christian match your talk? Are your actions the same at recovery meetings, church, home, and work?

- In what areas of your past have you used false humility to impress someone?

- Have any of your past business dealings been dishonest? Have you ever stolen things?

- List the ways you have been able to get out of your denial (distorted /dishonest thinking) into God's truth.

Spiritual Inventory Part 2

Principle 4: Openly examine and confess my faults to myself, to God, and to someone I trust.

> *"Happy are the pure in heart." (Matthew 5:8)*

Step 4: We made a searching and fearless moral inventory of ourselves.

> *"Let us examine our ways and test them, and let us return to the LORD." (Lamentations 3:40)*

Think About It

> *"Search me, O God, and know my heart; test my thoughts. Point out anything you find in me that makes you sad, and lead me along the path of everlasting life." (Psalm 139:23–24, TLB)*

The following list gives the second half of the list of our shortcomings (sins) that can prevent God from working effectively in our lives. Reading through it and searching your heart will help you get started on your inventory!

Your mind

"Do not conform any longer to the pattern of this world,
but be transformed by the renewing of your mind. Then you
will be able to test and approve what God's will is—his good,
pleasing and perfect will." (Romans 12:2)

- How have you guarded your mind in the past? Denial?
- Have you filled your mind with hurtful and unhealthy movies, television programs, internet sites, magazines, or books?
- Have you failed to concentrate on the positive truths of the Bible?

Your body

"Haven't you yet learned that your body is the home of
the Holy Spirit God gave you, and that he lives within you?
Your own body does not belong to you. For God has bought you
with a great price. So use every part of your body to give glory back
to God, because he owns it." (1 Corinthians 6:19–20, TLB)

- In what ways in the past have you mistreated your body?
- Have you abused alcohol and drugs? Food? Sex?
- What past activities or habits caused harm to your physical health?

Your family

"But if you are unwilling to obey the Lord, then decide today
whom you will obey. . . . But as for me and my family,
we will serve the Lord." (Joshua 24:15, TLB)

- In the past, have your mistreated anyone in your family?
- Who in your family do you have a resentment against?
- Who do you owe an amends to?
- What is the family secret that you have been denying?

Your church

> *"Let us not neglect our church meetings, as some people do, but encourage and warn each other, especially now that the day of his coming back again is drawing near." (Hebrews 10:25, TLB)*

- Have you been faithful to your church in the past?
- Have you been critical rather than active?
- In the past have you discouraged your family's support of their church?

As you continue your inventory, commit Psalm 139:23–24 (TLB) to memory and use it as a prayer:

> *Search me, O God, and know my heart; test my thoughts. Point out anything you find in me that makes you sad, and lead me along the path of everlasting life.*

Write About It

1. Your Mind

   - Since accepting Christ as your Higher Power, how has God transformed your mind (Romans 12:2)? What worldly standards have you given up?

- How have you used denial to attempt to guard your mind?

- Have you filled or are you filling your mind with hurtful and unhealthy movies, television programs, internet sites, magazines, or books?

- How have you failed to concentrate on the positive truths of the Bible? (Be specific.)

2. Your Body

- What past activities or habits caused harm to your physical health?

- In what ways have you mistreated your body?

- If you have abused alcohol, drugs, foods, or sex, how did they negatively affect your body?

- What have you done to restore God's temple?

3. Your Family

- Have you mistreated anyone in your family verbally, emotionally, or physically?

- Who in your family do you hold a resentment against? Why?

- Can you think of anyone to whom you owe amends? Why? (Don't worry about actually making them now! That's Principle 6.)

- What is the "family secret" that you have kept denying?

- How have relationships improved since you have been in recovery? (Be specific.)

4. Your Church

  • How would you rate your past participation in your church?
    _____ Very involved
    _____ Semiactive member
    _____ Sideline member
    _____ Attender
    _____ Went only on holidays
    _____ Never attended

  • Prior to your recovery, what was your main reason for going to church?

  • Have you ever tried to discourage any family members from church involvement? How? Why?

  • How has your commitment to your church increased since starting your recovery? (Give examples.)

AFTERWORD

When you complete all five lessons to the best of your ability, **CON-GRATULATIONS** are most definitely in order! Now you are ready to move to the next part of Principle 4: confessing your faults to God, yourself, and another person you trust. Taking this step will move you into freedom from your past. Not only will you find freedom as you share the secrets of your past with another person, but you will also receive the "perfect freedom" of Christ's complete forgiveness for all your past shortcomings and sins. That's Good News!

CELEBRATE RECOVERY® CREED

On the road to recovery we are changed when we accept
God's grace and forgiveness to solve our life problems.

We are changed when we become willing to share
our experience, strength and hope with one another.

Each of us needs repentance and recovery to live life
the way God intended.

We need fellowship and accountability to help us grow spiritually.

We utilize biblical truth that we need each other to grow
spiritually and emotionally.

By working the eight recovery principles we maintain
freedom from our life's hurts, habits and hang-ups.

This freedom creates peace, serenity, joy and most importantly,
a stronger personal relationship with our loving
and forgiving Higher Power, Jesus Christ!

Written by the brothers from the Celebrate Recovery ministry in
Sierra Conservation Center in Jamestown, California

Celebrate Recovery®

Getting Right with God, Yourself, and Others

Participant's Guide 3

John Baker is the founder of Celebrate Recovery®, a ministry born out of the heart of Saddleback Church. Over the last fourteen years, more than 7,500 individuals have gone through this Christ-centered recovery program at Saddleback. The Celebrate Recovery program is now being used in thousands of churches nationwide. In 1993, John and Pastor Rick Warren wrote the Celebrate Recovery curriculum which has been published and translated into several languages.

John began serving at Saddleback as a lay pastor in 1991. In 1992, he was asked to join the Saddleback Church staff as the Director of Small Groups and Recovery. In 1995, his responsibilities increased as he became the Pastor of Membership. In this position, John's responsibilities included pastoral counseling, pastoral care, Celebrate Recovery, support groups, small groups, and family, singles, and recreation ministries. In 1996, he oversaw the development of Saddleback's lay counseling ministry.

In June 1997, John became the Pastor of Ministries, responsible for the recruitment, training, and deployment of church members to serve in one of the more than 156 different ministries at Saddleback.

In 2001, Rick Warren asked John to become the Pastor of Celebrate Recovery. This is John's shape, his passion, and his calling. In addition, he is part of Saddleback's Purpose Driven team. John is a nationally known speaker and trainer in helping churches start Celebrate Recovery ministries. These ministries, in thousands of churches, reach out not only to their congregations but also to their communities in helping those dealing with a hurt, hang-up, or habit.

John and his wife Cheryl have been married thirty-five years and have served together in Celebrate Recovery since 1991. They have two adult children, Laura and Johnny. In 2004, Johnny and his wife, Jeni, gave John and Cheryl their first grandchild, Maggie.

UPDATED EDITION

Celebrate Recovery®

Getting Right with God, Yourself, and Others

PARTICIPANT'S GUIDE 3

A recovery program based on
eight principles from the Beatitudes

JOHN BAKER

FOREWORD BY RICK WARREN

ZONDERVAN™

GRAND RAPIDS, MICHIGAN 49530 USA

CONTENTS

FOREWORD BY RICK WARREN

You've undoubtedly heard the expression "Time heals all wounds." Unfortunately, it isn't true. As a pastor I frequently talk with people who are still carrying hurts from thirty or forty years ago. The truth is, time often makes things worse. Wounds that are left untended fester and spread infection throughout your entire body. Time only extends the pain if the problem isn't dealt with.

Celebrate Recovery® is a biblical and balanced program that can help you overcome your hurts, habits, and hang-ups. Based on the actual words of Jesus rather than psychological theory, this recovery program is more effective in helping people change than anything else I've seen or heard of. Over the years I've witnessed how the Holy Spirit has used this program to transform literally thousands of lives at Saddleback Church and help people grow toward full Christlike maturity.

Perhaps you are familiar with the classic 12-Step program of AA and other groups. While undoubtedly many lives have been helped through the 12 Steps, I've always been uncomfortable with that program's vagueness about the nature of God, the saving power of Jesus Christ, and the ministry of the Holy Spirit. So I began an intense study of the Scriptures to discover what God had to say about "recovery." To my amazement, I found the principles of recovery—in their logical order—given by Christ in His most famous message, the Sermon on the Mount.

My study resulted in a ten-week series of messages called "The Road to Recovery." During that series my associate pastor John Baker developed the four participant's guides, which became the heart of our Celebrate Recovery program.

As you work through these participant's guides, I trust that you will come to realize many benefits from this program. Most of all, however, my prayer for you is that, through Celebrate Recovery, you will find deep peace and lasting freedom in Jesus Christ as you walk your own road to recovery.

Dr. Rick Warren
Senior Pastor, Saddleback Church

INTRODUCTION

Congratulations! You are well on your way on your road to recovery. You began by "Stepping Out of Denial into God's Grace." Next you made the major commitment to your continued growth in recovery by completing your spiritual inventory. That took a lot of effort and courage, but you will see some of the rewards of all your hard work as you finish Principle 4. The truth found in James 5:16 will take on new meaning in your life: "Confess your sins to each other and pray for each other so that you may be *healed*" (italics added).

After you CONFESS your sins, you will receive God's complete and perfect forgiveness. When you ADMIT your wrongs and share your inventory with another, you will experience further healing. As you become entirely READY to work through Principle 5, you will experience God's VICTORY in removing your defects of character that may have plagued you all your life.

Principle 6 will show you how to make your AMENDS and offer FORGIVENESS, so that you can be a model of God's GRACE as you get right with others.

In His steps,
John Baker

THE ROAD TO RECOVERY

Eight Principles Based on the Beatitudes

By Pastor Rick Warren

1. **R**ealize I'm not God. I admit that I am powerless to control my tendency to do the wrong thing and that my life is unmanageable.
   "Happy are those who know they are spiritually poor."
   (Matthew 5:3)

2. **E**arnestly believe that God exists, that I matter to Him, and that He has the power to help me recover.
   "Happy are those who mourn, for they shall be comforted."
   (Matthew 5:4)

3. **C**onsciously choose to commit all my life and will to Christ's care and control.
   "Happy are the meek." (Matthew 5:5)

4. **O**penly examine and confess my faults to myself, to God, and to someone I trust.
   "Happy are the pure in heart." (Matthew 5:8)

5. **V**oluntarily submit to every change God wants to make in my life and humbly ask Him to remove my character defects.
   "Happy are those whose greatest desire is to do what God requires."
   (Matthew 5:6)

6. **E**valuate all my relationships. Offer forgiveness to those who have hurt me and make amends for harm I've done to others, except when to do so would harm them or others.
   "Happy are the merciful." (Matthew 5:7)
   "Happy are the peacemakers." (Matthew 5:9)

7. **R**eserve a daily time with God for self-examination, Bible reading, and prayer in order to know God and His will for my life and to gain the power to follow His will.

8. **Y**ield myself to God to be used to bring this Good News to others, both by my example and by my words.
   "Happy are those who are persecuted because they
   do what God requires." (Matthew 5:10)

Twelve Steps and
Their Biblical Comparisons

1. We admitted we were powerless over our addictions and compulsive behaviors, that our lives had become unmanageable.

   "I know that nothing good lives in me, that is, in my sinful nature.
   For I have the desire to do what is good, but I cannot carry it out."
   (Romans 7:18)

2. We came to believe that a power greater than ourselves could restore us to sanity.

   "For it is God who works in you to will and to act according
   to his good purpose." (Philippians 2:13)

3. We made a decision to turn our lives and our wills over to the care of God.

   "Therefore, I urge you, brothers, in view of God's mercy, to offer
   your bodies as living sacrifices, holy and pleasing to God—
   this is your spiritual act of worship." (Romans 12:1)

4. We made a searching and fearless moral inventory of ourselves.

   "Let us examine our ways and test them, and let us return
   to the LORD." (Lamentations 3:40)

5. We admitted to God, to ourselves, and to another human being the exact nature of our wrongs.

   "Therefore confess your sins to each other and pray for each other
   so that you may be healed." (James 5:16)

6. We were entirely ready to have God remove all these defects of character.

   "Humble yourselves before the Lord, and he will lift you up."
   (James 4:10)

7. We humbly asked Him to remove all our shortcomings.

   "If we confess our sins, he is faithful and just and will forgive us our sins and purify us from all unrighteousness." (1 John 1:9)

8. We made a list of all persons we had harmed and became willing to make amends to them all.

   "Do to others as you would have them do to you." (Luke 6:31)

9. We made direct amends to such people whenever possible, except when to do so would injure them or others.

   "Therefore, if you are offering your gift at the altar and there remember that your brother has something against you, leave your gift there in front of the altar. First go and be reconciled to your brother; then come and offer your gift." (Matthew 5:23–24)

10. We continued to take personal inventory and when we were wrong, promptly admitted it.

    "So, if you think you are standing firm, be careful that you don't fall!" (1 Corinthians 10:12)

11. We sought through prayer and meditation to improve our conscious contact with God, praying only for knowledge of His will for us and power to carry that out.

    "Let the word of Christ dwell in you richly." (Colossians 3:16)

12. Having had a spiritual experience as the result of these steps, we try to carry this message to others and to practice these principles in all our affairs.

    "Brothers, if someone is caught in a sin, you who are spiritual should restore him gently. But watch yourself, or you also may be tempted." (Galatians 6:1)

SERENITY PRAYER

If you have attended secular recovery programs, you have seen the first four lines of the "Prayer for Serenity." The following is the complete prayer. I encourage you to pray it daily as you work through the principles!

Prayer for Serenity

God, grant me the serenity
to accept the things I cannot change,
the courage to change the things I can,
and the wisdom to know the difference.
Living one day at a time,
enjoying one moment at a time;
accepting hardship as a pathway to peace;
taking, as Jesus did,
this sinful world as it is,
not as I would have it;
trusting that You will make all things right
if I surrender to Your will;
so that I may be reasonably happy in this life
and supremely happy with You forever in the next.
Amen.

Reinhold Niebuhr

Celebrate Recovery's Small Group Guidelines

The following five guidelines will ensure that your small group is a safe place. They need to be read at the beginning of every meeting.

1. Keep your sharing focused on your own thoughts and feelings. Limit your sharing to three to five minutes.
2. There is NO cross talk. Cross talk is when two individuals engage in conversation excluding all others. Each person is free to express his or her feelings without interruptions.
3. We are here to support one another, not "fix" another.
4. Anonymity and confidentiality are basic requirements. What is shared in the group stays in the group. The only exception is when someone threatens to injure themselves or others.
5. Offensive language has no place in a Christ-centered recovery group.

CONFESS

Principle 4: Openly examine and confess my faults to myself, to God, and to someone I trust.

> *"Happy are the pure in heart."* (Matthew 5:8)

Step 5: We admitted to God, to ourselves, and to another human being the exact nature of our wrongs.

> *"Therefore confess your sins to each other and pray for each other so that you may be healed."* (James 5:16)

Think About It

After writing an inventory, we must deal with what we have written. The first way we do that is to confess our sins to God. Let's review the acrostic for CONFESS.

Confess your shortcomings, resentments, and sins

God wants us to come clean. We need to admit that "what is wrong is wrong. We're guilty as charged." We need to own up to the sins we discovered in our inventory.

> *"He who conceals his sins does not prosper, but whoever confesses and renounces them finds mercy."* (Proverbs 28:13)

Obey God's directions

Principle 4 sums up God's directions for confessing our sins.
1. We confess our sins to God.

*"As surely as I am the living God, says the Lord, everyone will kneel
before me, and everyone will confess that I am God.' Every one of us,
then, will have to give an account of himself to God."*
(Romans 14:11–12, GNB)

2. We share them with another person whom we trust:

*"Therefore confess your sins to each other and pray for each
other so that you may be healed." (James 5:16)*

No more guilt

This step begins to restore our confidence and our relationships and
allows us to move on from our "rearview mirror" living. In Romans 8:1 we
are assured that "there is now no condemnation for those who are in Christ
Jesus."

*"All of have sinned; . . . yet now God declares us 'not guilty' . . .
if we trust in Jesus Christ, who . . . freely takes away our sins."*
(Romans 3:23–24, TLB)

The "CON" is over! We have followed God's directions on how to
confess our wrongs. Four very positive things start to happen after we
"FESS" up.

Face the truth

Recovery requires honesty! After we complete this principle we can
allow the light of God's truth to heal our hurts, hang-ups, and habits. We
stop denying our true feelings.

*"Jesus . . . said, 'I am the light of the world. Whoever follows
me will never walk in darkness, but will have the light of life.'"*
(John 8:12)

"Then you will know the truth, and the truth will set you free."
(John 8:32)

Ease the pain

"We are only as sick as our secrets!" When we share our deepest secrets we divide the pain and the shame. We begin to see a healthy self-worth develop, one that is no longer based on the world's standards, but on those of Jesus Christ.

> *"There was a time when I wouldn't admit what a sinner I was. But my dishonesty made me miserable and filled my days with frustration. . . . My strength evaporated like water on a sunny day until I finally admitted all my sins to you and stopped trying to hide them. I said to myself, 'I will confess them to the Lord.' And you forgave me! All my guilt is gone." (Psalm 32:3–5, TLB)*

Stop the blame

We cannot find peace and serenity if we continue to blame ourselves or others. Our secrets have isolated us from each other. They have prevented intimacy in all our relationships.

> *"Why do you look at the speck of sawdust in your brother's eye and fail to notice the plank in your own? How can you say to your brother, 'Let me get the speck out of your eye,' when there is a plank in your own? . . . Take the plank out of your own eye first, and then you can see clearly enough to remove your brother's speck of dust." (Matthew 7:3, PH)*

Start accepting God's forgiveness

Once we accept God's forgiveness we can look others in the eye. We understand ourselves and our past actions in a "new light." We are ready to find the humility to exchange our shortcomings in Principle 5.

> *"For God was in Christ, restoring the world to himself, no longer counting men's sins against them but blotting them out."*
> *(2 Corinthians 5:19, TLB)*

"But if we confess our sins, he will forgive our sins, because we can trust God to do what is right. He will cleanse us from all the wrongs we have done." (1 John 1:9, NCV)

Write About It

1. What wrongs, resentments, or secret sins are keeping you awake at night? Wouldn't you like to get rid of them?

2. What value do you see in confessing, in coming clean of the wreckage of your past?

3. As you obey God's directions for confession, what results do you expect God to produce in your life?

4. What freedom do you feel because of the words of Romans 8:1 and Romans 3:23–24? What specifically do the phrases "no condemnation" and "not guilty" mean to you?

5. After you complete Principle 4, you will find four areas of your life begin to improve. You will be able to face the truth, ease the pain, stop the blame, and start accepting God's forgiveness. In what areas of your life will each of these four positive changes help your recovery?

   I can be more honest with. . .

   I can ease my pain by. . .

I can stop blaming. . .

I can accept God's forgiveness because of. . .

ADMIT

Principle 4: Openly examine and confess my faults to myself, to God, and to someone I trust.

"Happy are the pure in heart." (Matthew 5:8)

Step 5: We admitted to God, to ourselves, and to another human being the exact nature of our wrongs.

"Therefore confess your sins to each other and pray for each other so that you may be healed." (James 5:16)

Think About It

People often ask me why they need to admit their wrongs to another person. There are three main reasons.

<u>W</u>hy admit my wrongs?

1. *We gain healing that the Bible promises.*
Look at James 5:16 again. God's Word tells us that we are to admit our wrongs, our sins, to *one another.* You do this not to receive their forgiveness, for God already forgave you when you confessed your wrongs and sins to Him. James 5:16 says to confess your sins to one another for *healing.*

Sharing our secrets, struggles, and failures with another is part of God's plan of our healing process. The road to recovery is not meant to be walked alone.

2. *We gain freedom.*

Our secrets have kept us in chains, bound up, frozen, and unable to move in all our relationships. Admitting our sins *snaps* the chains.

> *"They cried to the Lord in their troubles, and he rescued them!*
> *He led them from the darkness and the shadow of death and*
> *snapped their chains." (Psalm 107:13–14, TLB)*

3. *We gain support.*

When you share your inventory with another person, you get support. The person can keep you focused and provide feedback. He or she can challenge you when denial surfaces. Most important, the person will listen!

How do I choose someone?

1. Choose someone of the same sex as you whom you trust and respect.
2. Ask your sponsor or accountability partner. Just be sure they have completed Principle 4 (or Steps 4 and 5).
3. Set up an appointment with the person, a time without interruptions! It usually takes two to three hours to share your inventory.

Guidelines for your meeting

1. Start with prayer. Ask for courage, humility, and honesty. Here is a sample prayer:

> *God, I ask that You fill me with Your peace and strength during my sharing of my inventory. I know that You have forgiven me for my past wrongs, my sins. Thank You for sending Your Son to pay the price for me, so my sins can be forgiven. During this meeting help me to be humble and completely honest. Thank You for providing me with this program and* _____
> *(the name of the person with whom you are sharing your inventory). Thank You for allowing the chains of my past to be snapped. In my Savior's name I pray, Amen.*

2. Read the Principle 4 verses found on pages 25 and 26 in this participant's guide.
3. Keep your sharing balanced—weaknesses and strengths!
4. End in prayer. Thank God for the tools He has given to you and for the complete forgiveness found in Christ!

> *"But if we confess our sins, he will forgive our sins, because we can trust God to do what is right. He will cleanse us from all the wrongs we have done." (1 John 1:9, NCV)*

Write About It

1. In Principle 4 we are asked to give our inventory three times. Who are we to confess it to and why?

2. Most of us find it easier to confess our wrongs to ourselves and God. We seem to have more difficulty in sharing them with another person. What is the most difficult part for you? Why?

3. What is your biggest fear of sharing your inventory with another person?

4. List three people with whom you are considering sharing your inventory. List the pros and cons of each selection. Circle your final choice.

5. Pick a quiet location to share your inventory. List three places and circle the best one.

Now you are ready for one of the most freeing experiences of your life here on this earth! You will appreciate James 5:16 as never before. "Therefore confess your sins to each other and pray for each other so that you may be healed."

PRINCIPLE 4 VERSES

"Admit your faults to one another and pray for each other so that you may be healed." (James 5:16, TLB)

"You were dead in sins, and your sinful desires were not yet cut away. Then he gave you a share in the very life of Christ, for he forgave all your sins, and blotted out the charges proved against you, the list of his commandments which you had not obeyed. He took this list of sins and destroyed it by nailing it to Christ's cross. In this way God took away Satan's power to accuse you of sin, and God openly displayed to the whole world Christ's triumph at the cross where your sins were all taken away."
(Colossians 2:13–15, TLB)

"If we say that we have no sin, we are only fooling ourselves, and refusing to accept the truth. But if we confess our sins to him, he can be depended on to forgive us and to cleanse us from every wrong. (And it is perfectly proper for God to do this for us because Christ died to wash away our sins.)"
(1 John 1:8–9, TLB)

"For God was in Christ, restoring the world to himself, no longer counting men's sins against them but blotting them out. This is the wonderful message he has given us to tell others."
(2 Corinthians 5:19, TLB)

"A man who refuses to admit his mistakes can never be successful. But if he confesses and forsakes them, he gets another chance."
(Proverbs 28:13, TLB)

"Yes, each of us will give an account of himself to God."
(Romans 14:12, TLB)

"There was a time when I wouldn't admit what a sinner I was. But my dishonesty made me miserable and filled my days with frustration. All day and all night your hand was heavy on me. My strength evaporated like water on a sunny day until I finally admitted all my sins to you and stopped trying to hide them. I said to myself, 'I will confess them to the Lord.' And you forgave me! All my guilt is gone." (Psalm 32:3–5, TLB)

"So there is now no condemnation awaiting those who belong to Christ Jesus." (Romans 8:1, TLB)

READY

Principle 5: Voluntarily submit to every change God wants to make in my life and humbly ask Him to remove my character defects.

"Happy are those whose greatest desire is to do what God requires."
Matthew 5:6

Step 6: We were entirely ready to have God remove all these defects of character.

"Humble yourselves before the Lord, and he will lift you up."
(James 4:10)

Think About It

What does it mean to be entirely READY to have God remove our character defects?

Release control

God is a gentleman. In Principle 3 He didn't force His will on you. He waited for you to invite Him in! Now in Principle 5 you need to be entirely ready, willing to let God into every area of your life. He won't come in where He is not welcomed.

It has been said that "willingness is the key that goes into the lock and opens the door that allows God to begin to remove your character defects."

"Help me to do your will, for you are my God. Lead me in good paths, for your Spirit is good." (Psalm 143:10, TLB)

Easy does it

These principles and steps are not quick fixes! You need to allow time for God to work in your life. This principle goes further than helping you to stop doing wrong. It goes after the very defect that causes you to sin! *It takes time!*

> *"Commit everything you do to the Lord. Trust him to help you do it and he will."* (Psalm 37:5, TLB)

Accept the change

Seeing the need for change and allowing the change to occur are two different things. Principle 5 will not work if you are still trapped by your self-will. You need to be ready to accept God's help throughout the transition.

> *"So then, have your minds ready for action. Keep alert and set your hope completely on the blessing which will be given you when Jesus Christ is revealed. Be obedient to God, and do not allow your lives to be shaped by those desires you had when you were still ignorant."*
> *(1 Peter 1:13–14, GNB)*

Do replace your character defects

You spent a lot of time with your old hang-ups, compulsions, obsessions, and habits. When God removes one, you need to replace it with something positive, such as recovery meetings, church, service, and volunteering! If you don't, you open yourself for a negative character defect to return.

> *"When an evil spirit goes out of a person it travels over dry country looking for a place to rest. If it can't find one, it says to itself, 'I will go back to my house.' So it goes back and finds the house empty, . . . then it goes out and brings along seven other spirits even worse than itself, and they come to live there."* (Matthew 12:43–45, GNB)

Yield to the growth

Your old self-doubts and low self-esteem may tell you that you are not worthy of the growth and progress that you are making in the program. Yield to the growth—it is the Holy Spirit's work within you.

> *"The person who has been born into God's family does not make a practice of sinning, because now God's life is in him; so he can't keep on sinning, for this new life has been born into him and controls him—he has been born again." (1 John 3:9, TLB)*

Are you entirely ready—willing—to voluntarily submit to any and all changes God wants to make in your life? If you are, read the Principle 5a verses on page 32 and pray the following prayer:

> *Dear God, thank You for taking me this far in my recovery journey. Now I pray for Your help in making me be entirely ready to change all my shortcomings. Give me the strength to deal with all of my character defects that I have turned over to You. Allow me to accept all the changes that You want to make in me. Help me be the person that You want me to be. In Your Son's name I pray, Amen.*

Write About It

1. Have you released control? (If not, review Principle 3: "Consciously choose to commit all my life and will to Christ's care and control.")

   • List the areas of your life that you have been able to turn over and surrender to Jesus Christ.

- List the areas of your life that you are still holding on to, attempting to control them on your own power.

2. What does the phrase "easy does it" mean to you? What area of your recovery are you attempting to rush—looking for the "quick fix"?

3. Explain the differences in seeing a need for change and being entirely ready to accept positive change in your recovery.

4. It is very important that you allow God to replace your character defects with positive changes. What are some of the positive changes that you could make in your recovery? In your family? In your job?

5. Sometimes it is difficult for us in recovery to see the positive changes that God is making in our lives. Have you been able to accept and enjoy your growth? How?

PRINCIPLE 5A VERSES

"Humble yourselves before the Lord, and he will lift you up."
(James 4:10)

"So get rid of all that is wrong in your life, both inside and outside,
and humbly be glad for the wonderful message we have received,
for it is able to save our souls as it takes hold of our hearts."
(James 1:21, TLB)

"For I can never forget these awful years; always my soul will live
in utter shame. Yet there is one ray of hope: his compassion never
ends. It is only the Lord's mercies that have kept us from
complete destruction." (Lamentations 3:20–22, TLB)

"O loving and kind God, have mercy. Have pity upon me
and take away the awful stain of my transgressions. Oh, wash
me, cleanse me from this guilt. Let me be pure again."
(Psalm 51:1–2, TLB)

VICTORY

Principle 5: Voluntarily submit to every change God wants to make in my life and humbly ask Him to remove my character defects.

"Happy are those whose greatest desire is to do what God requires."
(Matthew 5:6)

Step 6: We were entirely ready to have God remove all these defects of character.

"Humble yourselves before the Lord, and he will lift you up."
(James 4:10)

Step 7: We humbly asked Him to remove all our shortcomings.

"If we confess our sins, he is faithful and just and will forgive us our sins and purify us from all unrighteousness." (1 John 1:9)

Think About It

How can you have VICTORY over your defects of character?

<u>**V**oluntarily submit</u>

Voluntarily submit to every change God wants me to make in my life and humbly ask Him to remove my shortcomings.

"Offer yourselves as a living sacrifice to God, dedicated to his service and pleasing to him. . . . Let God transform you inwardly by a complete change of your mind." (Romans 12:1–2, GNB)

In Principle 3 we made a decision to turn our lives over to God's will. Now "you are entirely ready to have God remove all your defects of character" (Step 6).

It is important to understand that Principle 5 is a process. Lasting change takes time. The remainder of this lesson outlines the process to have God make the positive changes in your life that you and He both desire.

Identify character defects

Identify which character defects you want to work on first. Go back to the wrongs, shortcomings, and sins you discovered in your inventory. Ask God to first remove those that are causing the most pain.

"In his heart a man plans his course, but the LORD determines his steps." (Proverbs 16:9)

Change your mind

When you become a Christian you are a new creation—a brand new person inside; the old nature is gone. But you have to let God (change) transform you by renewing your mind. The changes that are going to take place are a result of a team effort—your responsibility is to take the action to follow God's directions for change.

"Do not conform any longer to the pattern of this world, but be transformed by the renewing of your mind. Then you will be able to test and approve what God's will is—his good, pleasing and perfect will." (Romans 12:2)

Turn over character defects

Turn your character defects over to Jesus Christ. Relying on your own willpower has blocked your recovery. You have tried to change your hurts, hang-ups, and habits by yourself and were unsuccessful. "Let go; let God."

"Humble yourselves before the Lord, and he will lift you up."
(James 4:10)

"The Lord is faithful, and he will strengthen and protect you from
the evil one." (2 Thessalonians 3:3)

One day at a time

Recovery works one day at a time! Your lifelong hurts, hang-ups, and habits need to be worked on in twenty-four-hour increments. "Life by the yard is hard; life by the inch is a cinch."

"So don't be anxious about tomorrow. God will take care of your
tomorrow too. Live one day at a time." (Matthew 6:34, TLB)

Recovery is a process

Once you ask God to remove your character defects, you begin a journey that will lead you to new freedom from your past. Don't look for perfection; instead rejoice in steady progress.

"And I am sure that God who began a good work within you will
keep right on helping you grow in his grace until his task within you
is finally finished on that day when Jesus Christ returns."
(Philippians 1:6, TLB)

You must choose to change

To ask for help to change your hurts, hang-ups, and habits requires humility. We need to stop trying to make the changes on our power. We need to "humbly ask Him to remove all our shortcomings." We need to rely on His power to change us!

"God gives strength to the humble, . . . so give yourselves humbly to
God. Resist the devil and he will flee from you. And when you draw
close to God, God will draw close to you." (James 4:6–8, TLB)

Principle 5 Prayer

Dear God, show me Your will in working on my shortcomings. Help me not to resist the changes that You have planned for me. I need You to "direct my steps." Help me stay in today, not get dragged back into the past or lost in the future. I ask You to give me the power and the wisdom to make the very best I can out of today. In Christ's name I pray, Amen.

Write About It

1. As you *voluntarily* submit to every change God wants you to make in your recovery, how does Romans 12:1–2 help you know that real, positive change is possible?

2. In Principle 5 you need to ask God to help you identify the defects of character that you need to work on first. List the changes that you want to ask God to help you work on now. Will you work on them?

3. God's Word teaches us that real change comes from the changing of our minds. We must take the positive action required to follow God's directions. List the actions that you need to take to begin working on the defects of character that you listed in question 2.

ACTION PLAN

(Read the Principle 5b Verses on page 39.)

Defect of character:

I need to stop doing:

I need to start doing:

4. List the specific ways that you have turned from relying on your own willpower to relying on God's will for your life.

5. What does the phrase "one day at a time" mean to you and your recovery?

6. It has been stated that "Recovery is not perfection; it is a process." Do you agree with that? Why?

7. What does humility mean to you? How will being humble allow you to change?

Principle 5b Verses

"If we confess our sins, he is faithful and just and will forgive us our sins and purify us from all unrighteousness." (1 John 1:9)

"Don't copy the behavior and customs of this world, but be a new and different person with a fresh newness in all you do and think. Then you will learn from your own experience how his ways will really satisfy you." (Romans 12:2, TLB)

"If you want to know what God wants you to do, ask him, and he will gladly tell you, for he is always ready to give a bountiful supply of wisdom to all who ask him; he will not resent it."
(James 1:5, TLB)

"But he gives us more and more strength to stand against all such evil longings. As the Scripture says, God gives strength to the humble, but sets himself against the proud and haughty. So give yourselves humbly to God. Resist the devil and he will flee from you." (James 4:6–7, TLB)

"And when you draw close to God, God will draw close to you. Wash your hands, you sinners, and let your hearts be filled with God alone to make them pure and true to him." (James 4:8, TLB)

"Humble yourselves before the Lord, and he will lift you up."
(James 4:10)

"Now glory be to God who by his mighty power at work within us is able to do far more than we would ever dare to ask or even dream of—infinitely beyond our highest prayers, desires, thoughts, or hopes." (Ephesians 3:20, TLB)

AMENDS

———～———

Principle 6: Evaluate all my relationships. Offer forgiveness to those who have hurt me and make amends for harm I've done to others, except when to do so would harm them or others.

"Happy are the merciful." (Matthew 5:7)
"Happy are the peacemakers." (Matthew 5:9)

Step 8: We made a list of all persons we had harmed and became willing to make amends to them all.

"Do to others as you would have them do to you." (Luke 6:31)

———～———

Think About It

Making your amends is the beginning of the end of your isolation from others and God. The AMENDS acrostic will help you get started.

Admit the hurt and the harm

You need to once again face the hurts, resentments, and wrongs others have caused you, or wrongs that you have caused others. Holding on to resentments not only blocks your recovery but blocks God's forgiveness in your life.

"Do not judge others, and God will not judge you; do not condemn others, and God will not condemn you; forgive others, and God will forgive you." (Luke 6:37, GNB)

Make a list

Go back to your inventory sheets. In column 1 you will find the list of people who you need to forgive. In column 5 you will find the list of people to whom you owe amends. Are there any others you need to add?

"Treat others as you want them to treat you." (Luke 6:31, TLB)

Encourage one another

Before you make your amends or offer your forgiveness to others you need to meet with your accountability partner or a sponsor. He or she will encourage you and give you a valuable objective opinion, which will ensure that your motives stay on track.

"And let us consider how we may spur one another on toward love and good deeds." (Hebrews 10:24)

Not for them

You need to approach those to whom you are offering your forgiveness or amends humbly, sincerely, and willingly. Do not offer excuses or attempt to justify your actions. Focus only on your part. Don't expect anything back.

"Love your enemies and do good to them, lend and expect nothing back." (Luke 6:35, GNB)

Do it at the right time

This step not only requires courage, good judgment, and willingness, but a careful sense of timing! It is *key* at this time to prayerfully ask Jesus Christ for His guidance and direction.

"Each of you should look not only to your own interests, but also to the interests of others." (Philippians 2:4)

Start living the promises of recovery

As we complete this principle, we will discover God's gift of true freedom from our past. We will begin to find the peace and serenity that we have long been seeking. We will become ready to embrace God's purpose for our lives.

God promises, "I will repay you for the years the locusts have eaten" (Joel 2:25).

"If it is possible, as far as it depends on you, live at peace with everyone." (Romans 12:18)

Principle 6a Prayer

Dear God, I pray for willingness—willingness to evaluate all my past and current relationships. Please show me the people who I have hurt, and help me become willing to offer my amends to them. Also, God, give me Your strength to become willing to offer forgiveness to those who have hurt me. I pray for Your perfect timing for taking the action Principle 6 calls for. I ask all these things in Your Son's name, Amen.

Write About It

1. Once again you need to admit the past hurts—what others did to you and the harm that you caused to others. Explain how holding on to your past resentments and guilt has blocked your recovery. Be specific.

2. Next, you are ready to make your list. Use the following worksheet.

   List the names of those to whom you think you owe amends to in column 1. Then list those individuals who have hurt you and who you need to forgive in column 2. Keep this chart and see how God has increased your list within the next thirty days. Also, begin praying for the willingness and God's direction for you to complete this principle.

Amends List

I OWE AMENDS TO ...   I NEED TO FORGIVE ...

3. Who do you have on your recovery support team to encourage you as you make your amends and offer your forgiveness?

   SPONSOR:

   ACCOUNTABILITY PARTNERS:

4. What does the phrase "not for them" mean to you?

5. What does the phrase " don't expect anything back" mean to you?

6. Timing is so important in this step. List the individuals who could be possibly injured from your making an amends to them and why.

7. Go back to the "start living the promises" section of amends. List some of the promises of recovery that are coming true in your life!

FORGIVENESS

Principle 6: Evaluate all my relationships. Offer forgiveness to those who have hurt me and make amends for harm I've done to others, except when to do so would harm them or others.

"Happy are the merciful." (Matthew 5:7)
"Happy are the peacemakers." (Matthew 5:9)

Step 8: We made a list of all persons we had harmed and became willing to make amends to them all.

"Do to others as you would have them do to you." (Luke 6:31)

Step 9: We made direct amends to such people whenever possible, except when to do so would injure them or others.

"Therefore, if you are offering your gift at the altar and there remember that your brother has something against you, leave your gift there in front of the altar. First go and be reconciled to your brother; then come and offer your gift." (Matthew 5:23–24)

Think About It

Do you know the three kinds of forgiveness? To be completely free from your resentments, anger, fears, shame, and guilt, you need to give and accept forgiveness in all areas of your lives. If you do not, your recovery will be stalled and thus incomplete.

Have you accepted God's forgiveness?

Have you really accepted Jesus' work on the cross? By His death on the cross all your sins were canceled—*paid in full!* He exclaimed from the cross, "It is finished" (John 19:30).

"God puts people right through their faith in Jesus Christ. God does this to all who believe in Christ, because there is no difference at all: everyone has sinned and is far away from God's saving presence. But by the free gift of God's grace they are all put right with him through Jesus Christ, who sets them free. God offered him, so that by his sacrificial death he should become the means by which people's sins are forgiven through their faith in him." (Romans 3:22–25, GNB)

Have you forgiven others who have hurt you?

You must "let go" of the pain of the past harm and abuse caused by others. Until you are able to release it and forgive it, it will continue to hold you prisoner.

"Do not repay anyone evil for evil. Be careful to do what is right in the eyes of everybody. If it is possible, as far as it depends on you, live at peace with everyone." (Romans 12:17–18)

You may owe God an amends! Remember that the harm that others did to you was from their free will, not God's will.

*"After you have borne these sufferings a very little while, the God of all grace, who has called you to share his eternal splendor through Christ, will himself make you whole and secure and strong."
(1 Peter 5:10, PH)*

NOTE: If you have been the victim of sexual abuse, physical abuse, or childhood emotional abuse or neglect I am truly sorry for the pain you have suffered. I hurt with you. But you will not find the peace and freedom from your perpetrator until you are able to forgive that person. Remember, forgiving him or her in no way excuses the harm done against you. Forgiveness will allow you, however, to be released from the power that the person has had over you. I have rewritten Principle 6 (Steps 8 and 9) for you.

Step 8. Make a list of all persons who have harmed us and become willing to seek God's help in forgiving our perpetrators, as well as forgiving ourselves. Realize we've also harmed others and become willing to make amends to them.

Step 9. Extend forgiveness to ourselves and to others who have perpetrated against us, realizing this is an attitude of the heart, not always confrontation. Make direct amends, asking forgiveness from those people we have harmed, except when to do so would injure them or others.

Have you forgiven yourself?

You may feel that the guilt and shame of your past is just too much to forgive. This is what God wants you to do with the darkness of your past: "Come, let's talk this over! says the Lord; no matter how deep the stain of your sins, I can take it out and make you as clean as freshly fallen snow. Even if you are stained as red as crimson, I can make you white as wool! If you will only let me help you" (Isaiah 1:18–19, TLB).

Remember, "Therefore, there is now no condemnation for those who are in Christ Jesus" (Romans 8:1).

Write About It

1. As you look at the three kinds of forgiveness, which one of them was the easiest for you to accept? Why?

2. Which area of forgiveness was the most difficult for you to accept? Why?

3. What do the words of Christ found in John 19:30 ("It is finished.") mean to you?

4. What hurt(s) from a past relationship are you still holding on to?

5. How can you let go of the hurt(s)? Be specific.

6. Do you owe God an amends? When will you give it?

7. How have you been blaming God for the harmful actions that others took against you?

8. Have you forgiven yourself? What past actions in your life do you still feel guilt and shame about? (List them, pray about them, and work on them in the next lesson.)

PRINCIPLE 6A VERSES

"Treat others as you want them to treat you." (Luke 6:31, TLB)

*"Be gentle and ready to forgive; never hold grudges.
Remember, the Lord forgave you, so you must forgive others."
(Colossians 3:13, TLB)*

*"You, therefore, have no excuse, you who pass judgment on someone
else, for at whatever point you judge the other, you are condemning
yourself, because you who pass judgment do the same things."
(Romans 2:1)*

*"Do not judge, and you will not be judged. Do not condemn, and
you will not be condemned. Forgive, and you will be forgiven."
(Luke 6:37)*

*". . . and forgive us our sins, just as we have forgiven those who
have sinned against us." (Matthew 6:12, TLB)*

*"So what should we say about this? If God is with us,
no one can defeat us." (Romans 8:31, NCV)*

GRACE

Principle 6: Evaluate all my relationships. Offer forgiveness to those who have hurt me and make amends for harm I've done to others, except when to do so would harm them or others.

> *"Happy are the merciful." (Matthew 5:7)*
> *"Happy are the peacemakers." (Matthew 5:9)*

Step 9: We made direct amends to such people whenever possible, except when to do so would injure them or others.

> *"Therefore, if you are offering your gift at the altar and there remember that your brother has something against you, leave your gift there in front of the altar. First go and be reconciled to your brother; then come and offer your gift." (Matthew 5:23–24)*

Think About It

To complete Principle 6 we must make our amends, make restitution, offer our forgiveness, but most of all, we must receive and model Jesus Christ's freely given gift of GRACE.

> *"'My grace is enough for you. When you are weak, my power is made perfect in you.' So I am very happy to brag about my weaknesses. Then Christ's power can live in me. For this reason I am happy when I have weaknesses, insults, hard times, sufferings, and all kinds of troubles for Christ. Because when I am weak, then I am truly strong." (2 Corinthians 12:9–10, NCV)*

God's gift

Grace cannot be bought. It is a freely given gift by God to you and me. When we complete Principle 6, we are to offer (give) our amends and forgiveness and expect nothing back.

"All need to be made right with God by his grace, which is a free gift. They need to be made free from sin through Jesus Christ."
(Romans 3:24, NCV)

"Prepare your minds for service and have self-control. All your hope should be for the gift of grace that will be yours when Jesus Christ is shown to you." (1 Peter 1:13, NCV)

Received by our faith

We cannot work our way into heaven. Only by professing our faith in Christ as our Savior can we experience His grace and have eternal life. It is only through our faith in Christ that we can find the strength and courage needed for us to make our amends and offer our forgiveness.

"For it is by grace you have been saved, through faith— and this not from yourselves, it is the gift of God—not by works, so that no one can boast." (Ephesians 2:8–9)

"Through whom we have gained access by faith into this grace in which we now stand. And we rejoice in the hope of the glory of God." (Romans 5:2)

Accepted by God's love

God loved us while we were still sinning. Grace is the love that gives, that loves the unlovely and the unlovable. We can love others because God first loved us, and we can also *forgive* others because God first forgave us.

"Let us, then, feel very sure that we can come before God's throne where there is grace. There we can receive mercy and grace to help us when we need it." (Hebrews 4:16, NCV)

"Forgive us our debts, as we also have forgiven our debtors."
(Matthew 6:12)

"If you forgive men when they sin against you, your heavenly
Father will also forgive you." (Matthew 6:14)

Christ paid the price

Jesus loves us so much that He died on the cross so that all our sins, all our wrongs, are forgiven. He paid the price and sacrificed Himself for us so that we may be with Him forever. We also need to sacrifice—our pride and our selfishness. We must speak the truth in love and focus on our part in making amends or offering forgiveness.

"I do not set aside the grace of God, for if righteousness could be gained through the law, Christ died for nothing!" (Galatians 2:21)

"In Christ we are set free by the blood of his death, and so we have forgiveness of sins. How rich is God's grace." (Ephesians 1:7, NCV)

Everlasting gift

Once you have accepted Jesus Christ as your Lord and Savior, God's gift of grace is forever.

"And I am sure that God who began the good work within you will keep right on helping you grow in his grace until his task within you is finally finished on that day when Jesus Christ returns."
(Philippians 1:6, TLB)

"May our Lord Jesus Christ himself and God our Father encourage you and strengthen you in every good thing you do and say. God loved us, and through his grace he gave us a good hope and encouragement that continues forever." (2 Thessalonians 2:16, NCV)

Now you are ready to start modeling God's grace by working Principle 6.

1. Take the names of the individuals that you listed on your "Amends List" (page 43).
2. Highlight the ones you can take care of immediately.
3. Review them one more time with your sponsor or accountability partner to ensure that making an amends or offering your forgiveness to the individual would not injure them or another.
4. Pray, asking God to show you the right time to make the amends or offer your forgiveness. Read the Principle 6b verses on page 57.
5. Develop a plan for making amends to those on your list that you cannot make immediately. If someone on your list has died or you cannot locate him or her, you can write the person a letter and share it with your support team.

Principle 6b Prayer

Dear God, thank You for Your love, for Your freely given grace. Help me model Your ways when I make my amends to those I have hurt and offer my forgiveness to those who have injured me. Help me to set aside my selfishness and speak the truth in love. I pray that I would focus only on my part, my responsibility in the issue. I know that I can forgive others because You first forgave me. Thank You for loving me. In Jesus' name I pray, Amen.

Write About It

1. How has Jesus Christ used your weaknesses and turned them into strengths?

2. How can you receive God's gift of grace (Romans 5:2)?

3. How can you model God's gift of grace in making your amends?

4. In what ways have you experienced God's grace in your recovery?

5. God loved and accepted us while we were still sinners (Ephesians 2:5). How can you model that acceptance to those to whom you need to offer forgiveness or make amends?

6. In Principle 6 we are not trying to get even. Christ paid the price for all of our wrongs. What does "speaking the truth in love" mean to you?

7. Why is it important that you focus *only* on your part in making an amends or offering forgiveness?

8. List some of the things that God has shown you through working Principle 6.

Principle 6b Verses

"So if you are standing before the altar in the Temple, offering a sacrifice to God, and suddenly remember that a friend has something against you, leave your sacrifice there beside the altar and go and apologize and be reconciled to him, and then come and offer your sacrifice to God." (Matthew 5:23–24, TLB)

"If anyone says 'I love God,' but keeps on hating his brother, he is a liar; for if he doesn't love his brother who is right there in front of him, how can he love God whom he has never seen?"
(1 John 4:20, TLB)

"Love you enemies! Do good to them! Lend to them! And don't be concerned about the fact that they won't repay. Then your reward from heaven will be very great, and you will truly be acting as sons of God: for he is kind to the unthankful and to those who are very wicked." (Luke 6:35, TLB)

"There is a saying, 'Love your friends and hate your enemies.' But I say: Love your enemies! Pray for those who persecute you!"
(Matthew 5:43–44, TLB)

"Never pay back evil for evil. Do things in such a way that everyone can see you are honest clear through. Don't quarrel with anyone. Be at peace with everyone, just as much as possible."
(Romans 12:17–18, TLB)

"Pay all your debts except the debt of love for others—never finish paying that! For if you love them, you will be obeying all of God's laws, fulfilling all his requirements." (Romans 13:8, TLB)

Afterword

When you have completed all seven lessons to the best of your ability, CONGRATULATIONS are most definitely in order! The freedom you found by working Principles 4 through 6 can only come from God and a lot of courageous effort from you. You have taken a giant step toward "getting right with God, yourself, and others!"

Remember that recovery is a journey, a process. God and you are going to be working on the changes in your life for many years to come, one day at a time!

Now you are ready for the last two principles of the program. Principles 7 and 8 are going to show you how to continue "Growing in Christ While Helping Others."

CELEBRATE RECOVERY®
CREED

On the road to recovery we are changed when we accept
God's grace and forgiveness to solve our life problems.

We are changed when we become willing to share
our experience, strength and hope with one another.

Each of us needs repentance and recovery to live life
the way God intended.

We need fellowship and accountability to help us grow spiritually.

We utilize biblical truth that we need each other to grow
spiritually and emotionally.

By working the eight recovery principles we maintain
freedom from our life's hurts, habits and hang-ups.

This freedom creates peace, serenity, joy and most importantly,
a stronger personal relationship with our loving
and forgiving Higher Power, Jesus Christ!

Written by the brothers from the Celebrate Recovery ministry in
Sierra Conservation Center in Jamestown, California

Celebrate Recovery®

Growing in Christ While Helping Others

PARTICIPANT'S GUIDE 4

John Baker is the founder of Celebrate Recovery®, a ministry born out of the heart of Saddleback Church. Over the last fourteen years, more than 7,500 individuals have gone through this Christ-centered recovery program at Saddleback. The Celebrate Recovery program is now being used in thousands of churches nationwide. In 1993, John and Pastor Rick Warren wrote the Celebrate Recovery curriculum which has been published and translated into several languages.

John began serving at Saddleback as a lay pastor in 1991. In 1992, he was asked to join the Saddleback Church staff as the Director of Small Groups and Recovery. In 1995, his responsibilities increased as he became the Pastor of Membership. In this position, John's responsibilities included pastoral counseling, pastoral care, Celebrate Recovery, support groups, small groups, and family, singles, and recreation ministries. In 1996, he oversaw the development of Saddleback's lay counseling ministry.

In June 1997, John became the Pastor of Ministries, responsible for the recruitment, training, and deployment of church members to serve in one of the more than 156 different ministries at Saddleback.

In 2001, Rick Warren asked John to become the Pastor of Celebrate Recovery. This is John's shape, his passion, and his calling. In addition, he is part of Saddleback's Purpose Driven team. John is a nationally known speaker and trainer in helping churches start Celebrate Recovery ministries. These ministries, in thousands of churches, reach out not only to their congregations but also to their communities in helping those dealing with a hurt, hang-up, or habit.

John and his wife Cheryl have been married thirty-five years and have served together in Celebrate Recovery since 1991. They have two adult children, Laura and Johnny. In 2004, Johnny and his wife, Jeni, gave John and Cheryl their first grandchild, Maggie.

UPDATED EDITION

Celebrate Recovery®

Growing in Christ
While Helping Others

PARTICIPANT'S GUIDE 4

A recovery program based on
eight principles from the Beatitudes

JOHN BAKER

FOREWORD BY RICK WARREN

ZONDERVAN™

GRAND RAPIDS, MICHIGAN 49530 USA

Contents

FOREWORD BY RICK WARREN

You've undoubtedly heard the expression "Time heals all wounds." Unfortunately, it isn't true. As a pastor I frequently talk with people who are still carrying hurts from thirty or forty years ago. The truth is, time often makes things worse. Wounds that are left untended fester and spread infection throughout your entire body. Time only extends the pain if the problem isn't dealt with.

Celebrate Recovery® is a biblical and balanced program that can help you overcome your hurts, habits, and hang-ups. Based on the actual words of Jesus rather than psychological theory, this recovery program is more effective in helping people change than anything else I've seen or heard of. Over the years I've witnessed how the Holy Spirit has used this program to transform literally thousands of lives at Saddleback Church and help people grow toward full Christlike maturity.

Perhaps you are familiar with the classic 12-Step program of AA and other groups. While undoubtedly many lives have been helped through the 12 Steps, I've always been uncomfortable with that program's vagueness about the nature of God, the saving power of Jesus Christ, and the ministry of the Holy Spirit. So I began an intense study of the Scriptures to discover what God had to say about "recovery." To my amazement, I found the principles of recovery—in their logical order—given by Christ in His most famous message, the Sermon on the Mount.

My study resulted in a ten-week series of messages called "The Road to Recovery." During that series my associate pastor John Baker developed the four participant's guides, which became the heart of our Celebrate Recovery program.

As you work through these participant's guides, I trust that you will come to realize many benefits from this program. Most of all, however, my prayer for you is that, through Celebrate Recovery, you will find deep peace and lasting freedom in Jesus Christ as you walk your own road to recovery.

Dr. Rick Warren
Senior Pastor, Saddleback Church

INTRODUCTION

Congratulations! You have made it through the first six principles on your road to recovery. You began your journey by "Stepping Out of Denial into God's Grace." Then you faced the good and bad of your past by "Taking an Honest and Spiritual Inventory." And you just spent the last several months "Getting Right with God, Yourself, and Others."

Now you are ready to begin working on the last two principles along the road to recovery. These principles are much more than maintenance. As you practice them, they will help you continue "Growing in Christ While Helping Others," one day at a time!

Principle 7 is when you learn to take a daily INVENTORY and stand at the CROSSROADS of your recovery. You begin to live in newfound freedom in Christ. You learn that the best way to prevent a RELAPSE is to continue to grow in Christ through your quiet time and Bible study. In addition, Principle 7 will help you keep an "attitude of GRATITUDE."

And finally, in Principle 8 you understand how important it is to GIVE back to others what you have learned in your journey. Jesus will give you the courage to step out and say "YES" to helping newcomers and serving others.

In working with others, as sponsors or accountability partners, it is important for you to know the areas and reasons that can cause them to get stuck along their road to recovery. Lesson 25 includes the SEVEN REASONS WE GET STUCK IN OUR RECOVERIES.

After each lesson, there is an exercise for you to complete. Answer each question to the best of your ability. Don't worry about what you think the answer *should* be. Pray and then write down the answer from your heart. Remember John 8:32: "Then you will know the truth, and the truth will set you free."

After you have completed the exercise, share it with someone you trust. Your group, an accountability partner, or your sponsor (these are explained in Participant's Guide 2, Lesson 8) are all safe choices. You do not recover from your hurts, hang-ups, and habits by just attending recovery meetings. You must work and live the principles!

Now get ready for the rest of the journey that God has planned for you as you celebrate your recovery—one day at a time!

In His steps,
John Baker

THE ROAD TO RECOVERY

Eight Principles Based on the Beatitudes

By Pastor Rick Warren

1. **R**ealize I'm not God. I admit that I am powerless to control my tendency to do the wrong thing and that my life is unmanageable.
   "Happy are those who know they are spiritually poor."
   (Matthew 5:3)

2. **E**arnestly believe that God exists, that I matter to Him, and that He has the power to help me recover.
   "Happy are those who mourn, for they shall be comforted."
   (Matthew 5:4)

3. **C**onsciously choose to commit all my life and will to Christ's care and control.
   "Happy are the meek." (Matthew 5:5)

4. **O**penly examine and confess my faults to myself, to God, and to someone I trust.
   "Happy are the pure in heart." (Matthew 5:8)

5. **V**oluntarily submit to every change God wants to make in my life and humbly ask Him to remove my character defects.
   "Happy are those whose greatest desire is to do what God requires."
   (Matthew 5:6)

6. **E**valuate all my relationships. Offer forgiveness to those who have hurt me and make amends for harm I've done to others, except when to do so would harm them or others.
   "Happy are the merciful." (Matthew 5:7)
   "Happy are the peacemakers." (Matthew 5:9)

7. **R**eserve a daily time with God for self-examination, Bible reading, and prayer in order to know God and His will for my life and to gain the power to follow His will.

8. **Y**ield myself to God to be used to bring this Good News to others, both by my example and by my words.
   "Happy are those who are persecuted because they
   do what God requires." (Matthew 5:10)

Twelve Steps and Their Biblical Comparisons

1. We admitted we were powerless over our addictions and compulsive behaviors, that our lives had become unmanageable.

   "I know that nothing good lives in me, that is, in my sinful nature. For I have the desire to do what is good, but I cannot carry it out." (Romans 7:18)

2. We came to believe that a power greater than ourselves could restore us to sanity.

   "For it is God who works in you to will and to act according to his good purpose." (Philippians 2:13)

3. We made a decision to turn our lives and our wills over to the care of God.

   "Therefore, I urge you, brothers, in view of God's mercy, to offer your bodies as living sacrifices, holy and pleasing to God— this is your spiritual act of worship." (Romans 12:1)

4. We made a searching and fearless moral inventory of ourselves.

   "Let us examine our ways and test them, and let us return to the LORD." (Lamentations 3:40)

5. We admitted to God, to ourselves, and to another human being the exact nature of our wrongs.

   "Therefore confess your sins to each other and pray for each other so that you may be healed." (James 5:16)

6. We were entirely ready to have God remove all these defects of character.

   "Humble yourselves before the Lord, and he will lift you up." (James 4:10)

7. We humbly asked Him to remove all our shortcomings.

   *"If we confess our sins, he is faithful and just and will forgive us
   our sins and purify us from all unrighteousness." (1 John 1:9)*

8. We made a list of all persons we had harmed and became willing to make amends to them all.

   "Do to others as you would have them do to you." (Luke 6:31)

9. We made direct amends to such people whenever possible, except when to do so would injure them or others.

   *"Therefore, if you are offering your gift at the altar and there
   remember that your brother has something against you, leave your
   gift there in front of the altar. First go and be reconciled to your
   brother; then come and offer your gift." (Matthew 5:23–24)*

10. We continued to take personal inventory and when we were wrong, promptly admitted it.

    *"So, if you think you are standing firm, be careful
    that you don't fall!" (1 Corinthians 10:12)*

11. We sought through prayer and meditation to improve our conscious contact with God, praying only for knowledge of His will for us and power to carry that out.

    "Let the word of Christ dwell in you richly." (Colossians 3:16)

12. Having had a spiritual experience as the result of these steps, we try to carry this message to others and to practice these principles in all our affairs.

    *"Brothers, if someone is caught in a sin, you who are spiritual
    should restore him gently. But watch yourself, or you also
    may be tempted." (Galatians 6:1)*

SERENITY PRAYER

If you have attended secular recovery programs, you have seen the first four lines of the "Prayer for Serenity." The following is the complete prayer. I encourage you to pray it daily as you work through the principles!

Prayer for Serenity

God, grant me the serenity
to accept the things I cannot change,
the courage to change the things I can,
and the wisdom to know the difference.
Living one day at a time,
enjoying one moment at a time;
accepting hardship as a pathway to peace;
taking, as Jesus did,
this sinful world as it is,
not as I would have it;
trusting that You will make all things right
if I surrender to Your will;
so that I may be reasonably happy in this life
and supremely happy with You forever in the next.
Amen.

Reinhold Niebuhr

CELEBRATE RECOVERY'S SMALL GROUP GUIDELINES

The following five guidelines will ensure that your small group is a safe place. They need to be read at the beginning of every meeting.

1. Keep your sharing focused on your own thoughts and feelings. Limit your sharing to three to five minutes.
2. There is NO cross talk. Cross talk is when two individuals engage in conversation excluding all others. Each person is free to express his or her feelings without interruptions.
3. We are here to support one another, not "fix" another.
4. Anonymity and confidentiality are basic requirements. What is shared in the group stays in the group. The only exception is when someone threatens to injure themselves or others.
5. Offensive language has no place in a Christ-centered recovery group.

Lesson 19

CROSSROADS

Principle 7: Reserve a daily time with God for self-examination, Bible reading, and prayer in order to know God and His will for my life and to gain the power to follow His will.

Step 10: We continued to take personal inventory, and when we were wrong, promptly admitted it.

"So, if you think you are standing firm, be careful that you don't fall!" (1 Corinthians 10:12)

Think About It

Jesus says, "If you live as I tell you to, . . . you will know the truth, and the truth will set you free" (John 8:32, TLB). By working the principles and following Christ's directions, the foundation of your life has been rebuilt. You will undoubtedly see major changes in your life, if you haven't already! But now you are at the CROSSROADS of your recovery.

First Corinthians 10:12 warns us, "So, if you think you are standing firm, be careful that you don't fall!" Steps 10 through 12 (Principles 7 and 8) are where we will live out our recoveries for the rest of our time here on earth. They are much more than maintenance steps, as some have referred to them. These are the "how I want to live the rest of my life steps and principles."

As we begin to work Step 10[1], we will see that it is made up of three key parts, each one corresponding to the acrostic for this lesson, TEN.

---

1. Please note that though Step 10 and Principle 7 differ somewhat in their focus, both point toward the same result: the character and image of Christ in our daily life. This chapter will emphasize the step more than the principle, but in no way do we intend to discount the many benefits of daily living Principle 7.

<u>**T**ake time to do a daily inventory</u>

1. The *what*: "We continued to take personal inventory . . ."

"Let us examine our ways and test them, and let us return to the LORD." (Lamentations 3:40)

<u>**E**valuate the good and the bad parts of our day</u>

2. The *why*: " . . . and when we were wrong . . ."

"If we say that we have no sins, we are only fooling ourselves, and refusing to accept the truth . . . we are lying and calling God a liar, for he says we have sinned." (1 John 1:8–10, TLB)

<u>**N**eed to admit our wrongs promptly</u>

3. The *then what*: " . . . promptly admitted it."

"This is how I want you to conduct yourself in these matters. If you enter your place of worship and, about to make an offering, you suddenly remember a grudge a friend has against you, abandon your offering, leave immediately, go to this friend and make things right. Then and only then, come back and work things out with God." (Matthew 5:23–24, MSG)

Practice keeping a daily journal for one week. Write out your daily inventory—the good and the bad. Look for negative patterns, issues that you are repeatedly writing down and having to promptly make amends for! Share them with your sponsor or accountability partner, and set up an action plan for you—with God's help and power—to overcome them.

Write About It

1. Before you start working on Step 10, take a moment to reflect and list some of the changes in your life that have come from working the steps and principles with Jesus as your Higher Power.

   • How has your behavior changed?

   • What specific relationships have been restored or improved?

   • How has your relationship with Jesus grown since you began your journey of recovery?

   • List the new relationships that you have made along your journey.

2. In your own words, what does Step 10 mean to you?

    • The *what*: "We continued to take a personal inventory . . ."

    • The *why*: " . . . and when we were wrong . . ."

    • The *then what* : " . . . promptly admitted it."

3. Keep a daily journal over the next seven days. Record the good along with the bad. Write down victories and areas of needed growth. Look for patterns. Share them with your sponsor or accountability partner at the end of the week.

Your Step 10 Journal

Day One

Day Two

Day Three

Day Four

Day Five

Day Six

Day Seven

4. What did you learn by keeping your journal?

5. What areas did you identify as strengths?

6. What areas do you need to work on?

Suggestion: It's a Healthy Habit!

Keeping a daily journal is a key tool to help you stay on track on your road to recovery. You've done it for seven days, why stop now?

Daily Inventory

Principle 7: Reserve a daily time with God for self-examination, Bible reading, and prayer in order to know God and His will for my life and to gain the power to follow His will.

Step 10: We continued to take personal inventory and when we were wrong, promptly admitted it.

> *"So, if you think you are standing firm, be careful that you don't fall!" (1 Corinthians 10:12)*

Think About It

In Principle 7 and Step 10, we begin to apply what we have discovered in the first six principles and nine steps: We humbly live in reality, not denial; we have done our best to make amends for our past; we desire to grow daily in our new relationships with Jesus Christ and others.

God has provided us with a daily checklist for our new lifestyle. It's called the "Great Commandment":

> *"'Love the Lord your God with all your heart . . . soul and . . . mind.' This is the first and greatest commandment. And the second is like it: 'Love your neighbor as yourself.' All the Law and the Prophets hang on these two commandments." (Matthew 22:37–40)*

James 1:22 encourages us: "Do not merely listen to the word, and so deceive yourselves. Do what it says." When we practice the Great

Commandment, we become doers of God's Word, living examples of Christ. Our walk lines up with our talk! The apostle Paul lived that way. He says in 1 Thessalonians 1:5 (TLB), "Our very lives were further proof to you of the truth of our message."

There are three ways to do a Step 10 inventory.

Ongoing

We can do this periodically throughout the day. The best time to admit we are wrong is the exact time that we are made aware of it! Why wait? We need to make amends ASAP! We will sleep a lot better at night!

Daily

At the end of each day we need to look over our daily activities—the good and the bad. We need to search for where we might have harmed someone or where we acted out of anger or fear. The best way to do this is to keep a journal! Then the next morning as promptly as we can, we need to admit mistakes and make our amends.

Periodic

Every three months, get away for a "mini retreat." Bring your daily journal with you. Pray and read your daily entries. Ask God to show you areas in your life that you can improve over the next ninety days and the victories that you have made in the last ninety days!

The Bible gives us instructions on how to avoid the necessity of making an amends in Step 10:

> *"Intelligent people think before they speak; what they say is then more persuasive." (Proverbs 16:23, GNB)*

> *"Let no foul or polluting language, nor evil word nor unwholesome or worthless talk (ever) come out of your mouth, but only such (speech) as is good and beneficial to the spiritual progress of others." (Ephesians 4:29, AB)*

> *"A wise, mature person is known for his understanding. The more pleasant his words, the more persuasive he is."*
> *(Proverbs 16:21, GNB)*

"A word of encouragement does wonders!" (Proverbs 12:25, TLB)

*"If I had a gift of being able to speak in other languages
without learning them, and could speak in every language
there is in all of heaven and earth, but didn't love others,
I would only be making noise." (1 Corinthians 13:1, TLB)*

Step 10 daily action plan

1. Continue to take a daily inventory, and when you are wrong, promptly make your amends.
2. Summarize the events of your day in your journal.
3. Read and memorize one of the Step 10 verses (see above).
4. Work all steps and principles to the best of your ability.

The key verse for this lesson is Mark 14:38: "Watch and pray so that you will not fall into temptation. The spirit is willing, but the body is weak."

Principle 7a Prayer

Dear God, thank You for today. Thank You for giving me the tools to work my program and live my life differently, centered in Your will. Lord, help me to make my amends promptly and ask for forgiveness. In all my relationships today help me to do my part in making them healthy and growing. In Jesus' name I pray, Amen.

Write About It

1. What are some of the advantages of each of the three types of inventories in your recovery? How can they help you to "be careful that you don't fall"?

- Ongoing:

- Daily:

- Periodic (monthly, quarterly, or annually):

2. What do the following verses mean to you and how can they help you in this step?

   "From a wise mind comes careful and persuasive speech." (Proverbs 16:23, TLB)

   "Don't use bad language. Say only what is good and helpful to those you are talking to, and what will give them a blessing." (Ephesians 4:29, TLB)

"The wise man is known by his common sense, and a pleasant teacher is the best." (Proverbs 16:21, TLB)

"Anxious hearts are very heavy but a word of encouragement does wonders!" (Proverbs 12:25, TLB)

"If I had a gift of being able to speak in other languages without learning them, and could speak in every language there is in all of heaven and earth, but didn't love others, I would only be making noise." (1 Corinthians 13:1, TLB)

"Watch with me and pray lest the Tempter overpower you. For though the spirit is willing enough, the body is weak." (Mark 14:38, TLB)

3. What is your daily action plan for Step 10?

4. What are the recurring events or issues that you are constantly needing to make amends for?

    • With your family?

    • With your friends?

    • With those you work with?

    • With those in your church or recovery program?

Principle 7a Verses

"As God's messenger I give each of you God's warning: Be honest in your estimate of yourselves, measuring your value by how much faith God has given you." (Romans 12:3, TLB)

"Cling tightly to your faith in Christ and always keep your conscience clear, doing what you know is right." (1 Timothy 1:19, TLB)

"Cross-examine me, O Lord, and see that this is so; test my motives and affections too." (Psalm 26:2, TLB)

"We can justify our every deed but God looks at our motives." (Proverbs 21:2, TLB)

"A sensible man watches for problems ahead and prepares to meet them. The simpleton never looks, and suffers the consequences." (Proverbs 27:12, TLB)

"Keep a close watch on all you do and think. Stay true to what is right and God will bless you and use you to help others." (1 Timothy 4:16, TLB)

"So be careful. If you are thinking, 'Oh, I would never behave like that'—let this be a warning to you. For you too may fall into sin." (1 Corinthians 10:12, TLB)

"Come to terms quickly with your enemy before it is too late." (Matthew 5:25, TLB)

"My brothers and sisters, when you have many kinds of troubles, you should be full of joy, because you know that these troubles test your faith, and this will give you patience." (James 1:2–3, NCV)

"A relaxed attitude lengthens a man's life; jealousy rots it away." (Proverbs 14:30, TLB)

RELAPSE

Principle 7: Reserve a daily time with God for self-examination, Bible reading, and prayer in order to know God and His will for my life and to gain the power to follow His will.

Step 11: We sought through prayer and meditation to improve our conscious contact with God, praying only for knowledge of His will for us and power to carry that out.

"Let the word of Christ dwell in you richly." (Colossians 3:16)

Think About It

The best ways to prevent relapse can be summarized in the acrostic RELAPSE.

Reserve a daily quiet time

Principle 7 sums it up best: Reserve a daily time with God for self-examination, Bible reading, and prayer in order to know God and His will for my life and *gain the power* to follow His will.

> *"Watch and pray so that you will not fall into temptation. The spirit is willing, but the body is weak." (Mark 14:38)*

Evaluate

Your evaluation needs to include your physical, emotional, relational, and spiritual health. And don't forget the value of doing a "H-E-A-R-T" check. Are you

Hurting
Exhausted
Angry
Resentful
Tense

Special instructions for this step are found in Romans 12:3–17 (TLB): "Be honest in your estimate of yourselves. . . . Hate what is wrong. Stand on the side of the good. Love each other. . . . Be patient in trouble. . . . Do things in such a way that everyone can see you are honest clear through."

<u>**L**isten to Jesus</u>

We need to take a time-out from the world's "rat race" long enough to listen to our bodies, our minds, and our souls. We need to slow down enough to hear the Lord's directions.

> *"Test everything that is said to be sure it is true, and if it is, then accept it." (1 Thessalonians 5:21, TLB)*

> *"Let everyone be sure that he is doing his very best, for then he will have the personal satisfaction of work well done and won't need to compare himself with someone else." (Galatians 6:4, TLB)*

> *"Listen to the Lord. Hear what he is telling you." (Isaiah 1:10, TLB)*

<u>**A**lone and quiet time</u>

Jesus Christ spent time alone with His Father. You need to do the same. Set a daily appointment time to be alone with God. Listen carefully; learn how to hear God!

> *"Be still, and know that I am God." (Psalm 46:10)*

<u>**P**lug into God's power through prayer</u>

God's guidance and direction can start when your demands stop! Be specific in your prayer requests; pray about everything, asking for God's perfect will.

"Don't worry about anything; instead, pray about everything; tell God your needs and don't forget to thank him for his answers."
(Philippians 4:6, TLB)

Slow down long enough to hear God's answer

We can become impatient. We want our prayers answered now! We need to remember that our timing can be flawed, while God's timing is perfect!

"Listen to me. Keep silence and I will teach you wisdom!"
(Job 33:33, TLB)

"If you do this you will experience God's peace, which is far more wonderful than the human mind can understand. His peace will keep your thoughts and your hearts quiet and at rest as you trust in Christ Jesus." (Philippians 4:7, TLB)

Enjoy your growth

Rejoice and celebrate the small successes along your road to recovery! Always remember you're on a journey, a journey of several steps. Maintaining an "attitude of gratitude" is like taking spiritual vitamins.

Share your victories—no matter how small—with others in your group. Your growth will give others hope!

"Be joyful always, pray at all times, be thankful in all circumstances. This is what God wants from you in your life in union with Christ Jesus" (1 Thessalonians 5:16, GNB)

Here are a few final suggestions for preventing relapse:

1. Pray and read your Bible daily. Establish a specific time of day to have your "quiet time."
2. Make attending your recovery meeting a priority. Stay close to your support team.

3. Spend time with your family (if they are safe). If they are not, spend time with your church family.
4. Get involved in service. Volunteer!

Write About It

1. What are some of the ways (tools) that you have developed in your recovery to prevent relapse?

2. Do a H-E-A-R-T check right now. Are you

Hurting?

Exhausted?

Angry?

Resentful?

Tense?

3. Specifically, what do you do when you are

   Hurting?

   Exhausted?

   Angry?

   Resentful?

   Tense?

4. Rate your listening skills from 1 to 10, 10 being the best.

   - What are some ways that you think you could improve your listening skills with others?

   - What are some ways that you could improve your listening skills with God?

5. Describe what a "quiet time" means to you and why it is important.

6. How could you improve your prayer time? Be specific.

   When do you pray?

   Where do you pray?

7. After you pray, do you slow down long enough to hear God's answer? What does the word "meditation" in this step mean to you?

8. What are some of the other things that you do in your recovery to help you on your journey and prevent relapse?

9. I think we all agree that recovery is a joy, but it also requires hard work. What do you do to celebrate your recovery—even the small victories?

Lesson 22

GRATITUDE

Principle 7: Reserve a daily time with God for self-examination, Bible reading, and prayer in order to know God and His will for my life and to gain the power to follow His will.

Step 11: We sought through prayer and meditation to improve our conscious contact with God, praying only for knowledge of His will for us and power to carry that out.

"Let the word of Christ dwell in you richly." (Colossians 3:16)

Think About It

One of the greatest ways to work Principle 7 and to prevent relapse is to maintain an "attitude of gratitude."

In your prayers this week focus on your gratitude toward GOD, OTHERS He has placed in your life, your RECOVERY, and your CHURCH.

<u>Be thankful to God</u>

"Do not be anxious about anything, but in everything, by prayer and petition, with thanksgiving, present your requests to God."
(Philippians 4:6)

"Let us give thanks to the LORD for his unfailing love and wonderful deeds for men." (Psalm 107:15)

Be thankful for others

"Let the peace of Christ keep you in tune with each other, in step with each other. None of this going off and doing your own thing. And cultivate thankfulness. Let the word of Christ—the Message —have the run of the house." (Colossians 3:15–16, MSG)

Be thankful for your recovery

"As for us, we have this large crowd of witnesses around us. So then, let us rid ourselves of everything that gets in the way, and the sin which holds on to us so tightly, and let us run with determination the race that lies before us." (Hebrews 12:1, GNB)

Be thankful for your church

"Enter the Temple gates with thanksgiving." (Psalm 100:4, GNB)

Principle 7b Prayer

Dear God, help me set aside all the hassles and noise of the world to focus and listen just to You for the next few minutes. Help me get to know You better. Help me to better understand Your plan, Your purpose for my life. Father, help me live within today, seeking Your will and living this day as You would have me.

It is my prayer to have others see me as Yours; not just in my words but, more importantly, in my actions. Thank You for Your love, Your grace, Your perfect forgiveness. Thank you for all those You have placed in my life, for my program, my recovery, and my church family. Your will be done, not mine. In Your Son's name I pray, Amen.

Write About It

1. Why do you think it is important for you to maintain an "attitude of gratitude" in your recovery?

2. In what three areas of your recovery are you especially thankful for God's power? Try to think of areas of growth or positive change in you that only God could have accomplished.

   a.

   b.

   c.

3. Name three people God has placed in your recovery who you are grateful for and why.

   a.

   b.

   c.

4. What three areas of your recovery ministry, small groups, or other events are you thankful for? Why?

a.

b.

c.

5. List three things that you are thankful for in your church. Be specific.

a.

b.

c.

6. Congratulations! You have just completed your first *gratitude list*. Review it. How does it make you feel?

7. Let the individuals on your list know what an impact they have had on your recovery, and thank each of them personally!

PRINCIPLE 7B VERSES

"The whole Bible was given to us by inspiration from God and is useful to teach us what is true and to make us realize what is wrong in our lives; it straightens us out and helps us do what is right."
(2 Timothy 3:16, TLB)

"Now your attitudes and thoughts must all be constantly changing for the better."
(Ephesians 4:23, TLB)

"Be still, and know that I am God." (Psalm 46:10)

"Job, listen to this: Stop and notice God's miracles."
(Job 37:14, NCV)

"And if you leave God's paths and go astray, you will hear a Voice behind you say, 'No, this is the way; walk here.'"
(Isaiah 30:21, TLB)

"Oh, the joys of those who do not follow evil men's advice, who do not hang around with sinners, scoffing at the things of God. But they delight in doing everything God wants them to, and day and night are always meditating on his laws and thinking about ways to follow him more closely."
(Psalm 1:1–2, TLB)

"So now you can look forward soberly and intelligently to more of God's kindness to you when Jesus Christ returns. Obey God because you are his children; don't slip back into your old ways— doing evil because you knew no better." (1 Peter 1:13–14, TLB)

"Watch your step. Stick to the path and be safe. Don't sidetrack; pull back your foot from danger." (Proverbs 4:26–27, TLB)

"Watch with me and pray lest the Tempter overpower you. For though the spirit is willing enough, the body is weak."
(Mark 14:38, TLB)

"Be glad for all God is planning for you. Be patient in trouble, and prayerful always."
(Romans 12:12, TLB)

"You are living a brand new kind of life that is continually learning more and more of what is right, and trying constantly to be more and more like Christ who created this new life within you."
(Colossians 3:10, TLB)

"If you want to know what God wants you to do, ask him, and he will gladly tell you, for he is always ready to give a bountiful supply of wisdom to all who ask him; he will not resent it."
(James 1:5, TLB)

GIVE

Principle 8: Yield myself to God to be used to bring this Good News to others, both by my example and by my words.

"Happy are those who are persecuted because they do what God requires." (Matthew 5:10)

Step 12: Having had a spiritual experience as the result of these steps, we try to carry this message to others, and practice these principles in all our affairs.

"Brothers, if someone is caught in a sin, you who are spiritual should restore him gently. But watch yourself, or you also may be tempted." (Galatians 6:1)

Think About It

"Freely you have received, freely give." (Matthew 10:8)

What does it mean to GIVE?

God first

By placing God first in your life, you will realize that everything you have is a gift from Him. You realize that your recovery is not dependent on material things. It is built upon your faith and your desire to follow Jesus Christ's direction.

*"[He] did not even keep back his own Son, but offered him
for us all! He gave us his Son—will he not also freely give
us all things?" (Romans 8:32, GNB)*

*"You cannot serve two masters: God and money. For you
will hate one and love the other, or else the other way around."
(Matthew 6:24, TLB)*

I becomes we

The 12 Steps do not begin with the word "I." The first word in Step
1 is "we." The road to recovery is not meant to be traveled alone.

*"'Love the Lord your God with all your heart and with all your soul
and with all your mind.' This is the first and greatest commandment. And the second is like it: 'Love your neighbor as yourself.'"
(Matthew 22:37–39)*

*"Two are better off than one, because together they can work more
effectively. If one of them falls down, the other can help him up.
But if someone is alone . . . there is no one there to help him. . . .
Two men can resist an attack that would defeat one man alone."
(Ecclesiastes 4:9–12, GNB)*

Victories shared

God never wastes a hurt! Principle 8 gives us the opportunity to share
our experience and victories. "This is how it was for me. . . ." "This is what
happened to me. . . ." "This is how I gained the strength. . . ." "There's
hope for you."

*"Let us give thanks to the God and Father of our Lord Jesus Christ,
the merciful Father, the God from whom all help comes! He helps us
in all our troubles, so that we are able to help those who have all
kinds of troubles, using the same help that we ourselves have
received from God." (2 Corinthians 1:3, GNB)*

Example of your actions

In James 1:22 it says we are to be "doers of the word." But to be of help to another, we are to "carry the message in all our affairs."

You have all heard the term "Sunday Christians." Let us not become just "Friday night recovery buffs."

"My children, our love should not be just words and talk; it must be true love, which shows itself in action." (1 John 3:18, GNB)

The Lord spreads His message through the eight principles and the Christ-centered 12 Steps. We are the instruments for delivering the Good News. The way we live will confirm to others the sincerity of our commitment to our Lord, to the program, and to them! That's Principle 8.

"No one lights a lamp and then covers it with a washtub or shoves it under the bed. No, you set it up on a lamp stand so those who enter the room can see their way. . . . We're not hiding things; we're bringing everything out into the open. So be careful that you don't become misers. . . . Generosity begets generosity. Stinginess impoverishes."
(Luke 8:16–18, MSG)

Write About It

1. What does Matthew 10:8—"Freely you have received, freely give"—mean to you?

2. How has your attempt to put God first in your life changed your understanding of the word "give"?

3. Ecclesiastes 4:9 tells us that "two are better than one." List specific instances in your own recovery that you have seen this verse in action.

4. What are some of your recent victories that you could share with a newcomer?

5. In James 1:22 we are told to be "doers of the Word." How can you be a doer of the Word

   • among family and friends?

- in your recovery group?

- in your church?

- on the job?

- in your community?

YES

Principle 8: Yield myself to God to be used to bring this Good News to others, both by my example and by my words.

> *"Happy are those who are persecuted because they do what God requires." (Matthew 5:10)*

Step 12: Having had a spiritual experience as the result of these steps, we try to carry this message to others and to practice these principles in all our affairs.

> *"Brothers, if someone is caught in a sin, you who are spiritual should restore him gently. But watch yourself, or you also may be tempted." (Galatians 6:1)*

Think About It

When you reach this step you are ready to say YES to service.

Yield myself to God

Principle 8 sums up the *Y*: Yield myself to God to be used to bring this Good News to others, both by my example and by my words.

> *"If a Christian is overcome by some sin, . . . humbly help him back onto the right path, remembering that the next time it might be one of you who is in the wrong. Share each other's troubles and problems, and so obey our Lord's command." (Galatians 6:1–2, TLB)*

Example is what is important

Your walk needs to match your talk because your lifestyle reflects what you believe. Does your lifestyle show others the patterns of the world—selfishness, pride, and lust—or does it reflect the love, humility, and service of Jesus Christ?

"Arouse the love that comes from a pure heart, a clear conscience, and a genuine faith." (1 Timothy 1:5, GNB)

"Let us not love with words or tongue but with actions and in truth." (1 John 3:18)

Serve others as Jesus Christ did

When you have reached Principle 8, you are ready to pick up the "Lord's towel," the one with which He washed the disciples' feet in the upper room.

"And since I, the Lord and Teacher, have washed your feet, you ought to wash each other's feet. I have given you an example to follow: do as I have done to you." (John 13:14–15, TLB)

How You Can Say YES

1. *Be an accountability partner.* Look for someone in your small group who will agree to encourage and support you as you work through the principles. You agree to do the same for that person. You hold one another accountable for working an honest program.

2. *Be a sponsor.* Sponsors are people who have worked the principles or the steps. Their job is to guide newcomers on their journey through the program, to give a gentle nudge when they are procrastinating or slow them down when they are rushing through a step. Sponsors do so by sharing their personal journey on their road to recovery.

3. *Be involved in Celebrate Recovery and your church.* There are many opportunities for service in this recovery ministry and in your church.

You have come to the fork in your road to recovery.

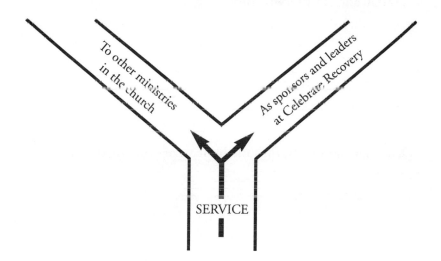

Remember, "You can't keep it unless you give it away!"

Principle 8 Prayer

Dear Jesus, as it would please You, bring me someone today whom I can serve. Amen.

Write About It!

1. If you knew that you couldn't fail, what would you like to do most for God in helping others?

2. What are some ways you can pick up the Lord's towel (John 13:14–15) today and start serving others?

3. What does the illustration of the fork in your road to recovery say to you?

4. In the words of Step 12, how will you "practice these principles in all [y]our affairs"?

5. Describe what the phrase "You can't keep it unless you give it away" means in your recovery.

6. Create your own action plan for Principle 8.

   I am going to explore opportunities to serve in the following areas:

   a.

   b.

   c.

PRINCIPLE 8 VERSES

*"What a wonderful God we have—he is the Father of
our Lord Jesus Christ, the source of every mercy, and the one who
so wonderfully comforts and strengthens us in our hardships and
trials. And why does he do this? So that when others are troubled,
needing our sympathy and encouragement, we can pass on to
them this same help and comfort God has given us."
(2 Corinthians 1:3–4, TLB)*

*"But watch out! Be very careful never to forget what you have
seen God doing for you. May his miracles have a deep and
permanent effect upon your lives! Tell your children and
your grandchildren about the glorious miracles he did."
(Deuteronomy 4:9, TLB)*

*"In the same way, faith by itself, if it is not accompanied
by action, is dead." (James 2:17)*

*"Live and act in a way worthy of those who have been chosen for
such wonderful blessings as these." (Ephesians 4:1, TLB)*

*"But we Christians have no veil over our faces; we can be
mirrors that brightly reflect the glory of the Lord."
(2 Corinthians 3:18, TLB)*

*"In response to all he has done for us, let us outdo each other
in being helpful and kind to each other and in doing good."
(Hebrews 10:24, TLB)*

*"When God's children are in need, you be the one to help them
out. . . . Don't just pretend that you love others; really love them.
Hate what is wrong. Stand on the side of the good."
(Romans 12:13, 9, TLB)*

*"Dear brothers, if a Christian is overcome by some sin,
you who are godly should gently and humbly help him back
onto the right path, remembering that next time it might be
one of you who is in the wrong." (Galatians 6:1, TLB)*

*"Two can accomplish more than twice as much as one,
for the results can be much better. If one falls, the other pulls
him up; but if a man falls when he is alone, he's in trouble. . . .
And one standing alone can be attacked and defeated, but two
can stand back-to-back and conquer; three is even better,
for a triple-braided cord is not easily broken."
(Ecclesiastes 4:9–12, TLB)*

SEVEN REASONS WE GET STUCK

As you complete your journey, you will discover the rewards of sponsoring newcomers. Your role as a sponsor will be to help others along their journey on the road to recovery by guiding them through the principles and steps. Your task is not to pick them up and carry them through the steps, but to stand alongside them as they complete their journey.

At times, you may need to slow them down when they are moving through the steps too quickly; or you may need to speed them up when they get stuck along the side of the road. There are seven major areas in which I have seen individuals get "stuck" at some point in their recoveries. It is important that you are familiar with each of them so you help them get "unstuck."

You have not completely worked the previous principle

Perhaps you are trying to move through the principles too quickly. Slow down! Give God time to work! Remember, this program is a process.

"Since we live by the Spirit, let us keep in step with the Spirit."
(Galatians 5:25)

You have not completely surrendered your life and your will to the Lord

Perhaps you are trusting Jesus with the "big" things, but you still think you can handle the "small" things.

"For good judgment and common sense, trust in the Lord completely; don't ever trust in yourself. In everything you do, put God first, and he will direct you and crown your efforts with success." (Proverbs 3:5–6, TLB)

You have not accepted Jesus' work on the cross for your forgiveness

You may have forgiven others, but you think your sin is too big to be forgiven.

"But if we confess our sins to him, he can be depended on to forgive us . . . from every wrong." (1 John 1:9, TLB)

"So overflowing is his kindness towards us that he took away all our sins through the blood of his Son, by whom we are saved." (Ephesians 1:7, TLB)

Have you forgiven yourself?
Remember,

"Therefore, there is now no condemnation for those who are in Christ Jesus." (Romans 8:1)

You really have not forgiven others who have harmed you

You must "let go" of the pain of past harm and abuse. Until you are able to release it, forgive it, it will continue to hold you as its prisoner.

"After you have suffered a little while, our God, who is full of kindness through Christ, will give you his eternal glory. He personally will pick you up, and set you firmly in place and make you stronger than ever." (1 Peter 5:10–11, TLB)

You are afraid of the risk in making the necessary change

You may be paralyzed by the fear of failure. You may fear intimacy because of the fear of rejection or of being hurt again. You may resist change (growth) because of the fear of the unknown.

"Fear not, for I am with you. Do not be dismayed. . . .
I will strengthen you; I will help you; I will uphold you
with my victorious right hand." (Isaiah 41:10, TLB)

"That is why we can say without any doubt or fear,
'The Lord is my Helper and I am not afraid of anything
that mere man can do to me.'" (Hebrews 13:6, TLB)

You are not willing to "own" your responsibility

You need to take responsibility for your past in a broken relationship, a damaged friendship, with a distant child or parent, and so forth.

"Examine me, O God, and know my mind; test me, and discover . . .
if there is any evil in me and guide me in the everlasting way."
(Psalm 139:23, GNB)

You have not developed an effective support team

Do you have a sponsor or an accountability partner? Do you have the phone numbers of others in your small group? Have you volunteered for a commitment to your recovery ministry?

"Be with wise men and become wise. Be with evil men
and become evil." (Proverbs 13:20, TLB)

"Dear brothers, you have been given freedom: not freedom
to do wrong, but freedom to love and serve each another."
(Galatians 5:13, TLB)

"Share each other's troubles and problems, and so obey
our Lord's command." (Galatians 6:2, TLB)

AFTERWORD

CONGRATULATIONS! You have completed all eight principles and all 12 Steps! I do not have to tell you that was not an easy accomplishment! There are many rewards found in this Christ-centered program. It is important that you share your "miracle" with others. You are a living example of God's grace. I pray for your continued growth in Christ, your recovery, and your service to others. Below please find Celebrate Recovery's Daily Action Plan for Serenity.

In His steps,
John Baker

Celebrate Recovery's Daily Action Plan for Serenity

1. Daily, continue to take an inventory. When you are wrong, promptly admit it.
2. Daily, study God's Word and pray asking God to guide you and help you apply His teaching and will in your life.
3. Daily, work and live the eight principles to the best of your ability, always looking for new opportunities to help and serve others—not just at your recovery meetings but in all areas of your life.

CELEBRATE RECOVERY® CREED

On the road to recovery we are changed when we accept
God's grace and forgiveness to solve our life problems.

We are changed when we become willing to share
our experience, strength and hope with one another.

Each of us needs repentance and recovery to live life
the way God intended.

We need fellowship and accountability to help us grow spiritually.

We utilize biblical truth that we need each other to grow
spiritually and emotionally.

By working the eight recovery principles we maintain
freedom from our life's hurts, habits and hang-ups.

This freedom creates peace, serenity, joy and most importantly,
a stronger personal relationship with our loving
and forgiving Higher Power, Jesus Christ!

Written by the brothers from the Celebrate Recovery ministry in
Sierra Conservation Center in Jamestown, California

We want to hear from you. Please send your comments about this book to us in care of zreview@zondervan.com. Thank you.

ZONDERVAN™

GRAND RAPIDS, MICHIGAN 49530 USA

WWW.ZONDERVAN.COM